BLACK CATS QUIZ BOOK

Published by twocan

©2017. Published by twocan under licence from Sunderland AFC.

ISBN: 978-1-911502-69-2

PICTURE CREDITS: Action Images, Mirrorpix, Press Association, Sunderland AFC.

COMPILED BY ROB MASON

FOREWORD

From the moment I walked into Roker Park back in 1990 to sign for Denis Smith, I started learning all about this fantastic part of the country. I learnt that Sunderland was by the sea, which I hadn't realised, and I learnt that people told it as it was. If I hadn't had a good game, I expected to be told so. Mind, if I had got stuck in though, and showed our fans I cared, I knew that people would stick by me. A mutual respect between myself and supporters was soon firmly established and that rapport has never waned.

I learned that people in Sunderland don't just breathe sea-air, they live and breathe the football club. That is why in good times and bad the main topic of conversation on Wearside is always the Lads.

This book will tap into that knowledge. Simon Grayson's current day squad are featured, as are the teams I played for through the nineties, the cup final team of '92, the Play-off side of '98 and the title winners of '96 and '99 - and that's just one decade. There are almost as many quizzes here as we got points in 1998-99 and if you're half as good at picking up points as that team was, you'll do well here.

Kevin Ball

INTRODUCTION

Being a Sunderland supporter myself, I'm well aware of how knowledgeable Sunderland fans are. Hardly surprisingly, people who live and breathe the club know a lot about it.

This set of 100 quizzes includes some questions that every supporter is likely to know the answers to, some that will stretch the grey matter a little and some that will tease even the red and white die-hards amongst you.

I've often made questions multi-choice, but not always. Some questions have answers that are simple facts, that if you don't know without a prompt, it's time to learn. Hopefully this book will entertain you and ideally make you realise a few things that you might not know even if you are an SAFC brain-box.

What comes out of many of these quizzes is how many tremendously dedicated players and managers the club has had throughout its history. That is a testament to the club itself and what it represents in the community. Taking on this book shows you are a similarly dedicated supporter.

The quizzes cover a wide range of the club's players, managers and major events. It is not a guide to the club though, so your favourite player might not have a quiz dedicated solely to him.

See how many of the 1000 questions you can get right. Can you get 627 right? If so, you'll have equalled Jimmy Montgomery's record number of appearances. If you know your stuff on Sunderland, it's a good target to set. From my point of view, setting the questions was quite a challenge. As a compiler you don't want to make them too hard or too easy. Hopefully everyone will be able to answer at least some questions, but equally the experts amongst you won't find them all too simple.

I'd like to thank Kevin Ball for contributing the Foreword. If you want someone to take on a challenge, Bally's your man.

I'd also like to acknowledge many sources, including Sunderland the Complete Record, a book I produced with Mike Gibson and Barry Jackson, All the Lads, Rothmans / Sky Sports Yearbooks, Breedon's 'Football Managers' book and the England Online website.

Rob Mason

QUIZ 1
GOALKEEPERS

1. Which goalkeeper holds Sunderland's appearance record?

2. Which teenager kept goal for Sunderland at Wembley?

3. Who is the only goalkeeper to be capped by England while with Sunderland?

4. Who was the first Sunderland goalkeeper to save a penalty at St. James' Park after Thomas Sorensen?

5. Who kept goal for Sunderland twice at Wembley?

6. Who was the first goalkeeper to play in an FA Cup final for Sunderland?

7. Which goalkeeper played in Sunderland's first Premier League game?

8. Which Sunderland goalkeeper conceded eleven goals in one game including a penalty shoot-out?

9. Which goalkeeper debuted in the game Sunderland won promotion in 2005?

10. Simon Mignolet, Keiren Westwood and which other 'keeper appeared in the Premier League for Sunderland in 2011-12?

QUIZ 2
ENGLAND AT THE SOL

11. Who were the first country England played at the Stadium of Light?

12. In what year?

13. Kevin Phillips played in that game, but who was the other Sunderland player selected for the squad for that game, but not the match?

14. Brazil played at the second England international at the Sol in 1999, at what level?

15. In what year did England play Turkey at the SoL?

16. Apart from David Beckham who scored for England in that 2-0 win?

17. After England lost 3-5 to Italy at Under-20 level in 2002 who were the visitors in the first Under-21 international at the SoL the following year?

18. Who did England meet in 2016?

19. Who scored in the opening minutes?

20. Which England player scored an own goal?

JOE BOLTON

21. What position did Joe Bolton play?

22. In which year did he make his debut against Watford?

23. Did he play in the FA Cup run of 1973?

24. Who were Sunderland playing when he scored twice and then missed a penalty?

25. How many times was Joe sent off while playing for Sunderland?

26. Which trophy did Joe win while with Sunderland?

27. In which year was that trophy won?

28. Which manager sold him to Middlesbrough?

29. Which club did he move onto from 'Boro?

30. Which club did he become player/manager of in the late 1980s?

STAN ANDERSON

31. How many players have played more games for Sunderland than Stan?

32. In which year did he make his debut?

33. Who did he score twice against in the FA Cup in 1961?

34. Who was he sent off against on England Under-23 duty?

35. How many full England caps did he win?

36. How many FA Cup semi-finals did Stan play in for Sunderland?

37. Which club was Anderson with when Sunderland staged his Testimonial?

38. Who did he captain to promotion in 1965?

39. Which Greek team was he manager of when Sunderland won the FA Cup in 1973?

40. Which two future Sunderland managers did he coach and manage at Bolton Wanderers?

CHARLIE HURLEY

41.   Which manager signed Charlie for Sunderland?

42.   Who was manager when he left?

43.   How many managers did he play for at Sunderland?

44.   In which season was Charlie said to be running
      the team in the first half of the campaign?

45.   Which club was Charlie manager of when he returned
      to Roker Park during the 1973 FA Cup run?

46.   Who was Footballer of the Year in the year Charlie
      was runner-up?

47.   In which year did Charlie captain Sunderland to promotion?

48.   What permanent tribute to Charlie stands outside
      the Stadium of Light?

49.   Which player took Charlie's record as Sunderland's
      most capped player?

50.   Which accolade was given to Charlie in the Club's
      centenary year in 1979?

QUIZ 6
LEE CATTERMOLE

51.   With which club did Lee make his debut?

52.   Who did he appear against as a sub in a UEFA Cup final?

53.   Who else did he play for before coming to Sunderland?

54.   Which manager signed him for Sunderland?

55.   In which year did Lee debut for Sunderland?

56.   Who was his Sunderland debut against?

57.   Which Albanian international did he form a dominant partnership with in his opening months at Sunderland?

58.   Who did he score his first goal for Sunderland against?

59.   In which year did he reach the final of the European Under-21 Championship with England?

60.   In which year was he the North East Football Writers' Association Player of the Year?

BOBBY KERR

61. What was Bobby's nickname?

62. In which year had he played in the FA Youth Cup final?

63. Who did he score against on his debut?

64. How many goals did he score in his first eleven games?

65. Which club did Bobby score against during the 1973 Cup run?

66. What record does he share with Raich Carter?

67. What is the name of his brother who made almost 400 league appearances and managed three league clubs?

68. Who did Bobby move on to in 1979?

69. Who else did he play for?

70. In 1971-72, who were Sunderland playing when Bobby scored a classic volley from a Dennis Tueart corner?

COLIN SUGGETT

71. In which year did Colin debut against Stoke?

72. Which trophy did Colin captain Sunderland to?

73. How many games did he start for Sunderland, 70, 80 or 90?

74. How many goals did he score for Sunderland, 25, 35 or 45?

75. Which club paid their record fee of £95,000 to sign him in 1969?

76. Which club paid their record fee to sign him in 1973?

77. Which other North East team did he play for and serve as caretaker manager?

78. Which cup final did he play in in 1970?

79. Which cup final did he play in in 1975?

80. Colin scored twice on his WBA debut, away to which team who wore red and white stripes?

QUIZ 9
BOBBY GURNEY

81. Bobby is Sunderland's record goalscorer.
     How many did he score?

82. How many games did he play for Sunderland,
     390, 400 or 410?

83. Where was he born?

84. How many years in a row was he Sunderland's top scorer?

85. How many goals did he score in the 1936 title-winning
     season, 29, 30 or 31?

86. He scored Sunderland's first-ever goal at Wembley.
     Who was it against?

87. How many official England caps did he win?

88. Who were the only club he managed outside the North East?

89. Who did he score five goals in a game against?

90. How many goals did he score on the day Sunderland
     sealed the league title in 1936?

IAN PORTERFIELD

91.   Who did Sunderland sign Ian from?

92.   In which season did he debut in a 3-3 draw
      with Newcastle United?

93.   Was his cup final winner scored with his right foot or his left?

94.   What was the name of the book he published
      after the cup triumph?

95.   Which club did he join on loan from Sunderland?

96.   At which club did he play for his old Sunderland
      teammate Len Ashurst?

97.   When he managed in his native Scotland, who did Ian
      take over from at Aberdeen?

98.   At which London club was Ian managing when he became
      the first Premier League manager to be sacked?

99.   Which was the first of five international teams he managed?

100. Which country was Ian manager of when he passed away
      in 2007 at the age of 61?

DENNIS TUEART

101. How many goals did Dennis score during
the 1973 cup-winning run?

102. Who did he score a hat-trick against in the season
after the cup win?

103. He made his debut against Sheffield Wednesday
on Boxing Day in which year?

104. He scored Sunderland's last top-flight goal before
the 1973 cup win, with a winner away to which club?

105. In which season was he Sunderland's joint top league scorer?

106. Against which side did he become Sunderland's
first goal-scorer in European football?

107. When he was transferred to Manchester City along
with Mick Horswill, which City player moved to Sunderland
as part of the same deal?

108. Who did he score against with a spectacular bicycle kick
at Wembley in the 1976 League Cup final?

109. Who did he score against for England at Wembley
in the same year?

110. When he signed for New York Cosmos, who was he bought
to replace?

SUBS

111. Who was Sunderland's substitute in the 1973 FA Cup final?

112. Who was the first man named as a sub by Sunderland?

113. Sunderland were away to Leeds in that game in the opening match of the season. What was the year?

114. Who was the first sub to actually be used by Sunderland?

115. Who did he replace?

116. Who was the manager who made the substitution?

117. Who was the first sub to score?

118. Who was the sub who marked his debut in March 1968 by becoming the first sub to score at Roker Park?

119. Who was the 16-year-old who came off the bench to become Sunderland's youngest scorer with a late winner in a 4-3 win over Preston in 1971?

120. Which sub scored a dramatic last-minute winner against Manchester City on New Year's Day 2012?

QUIZ 13
AIDEN McGEADY

121. Who did Aiden make his Sunderland debut against?

122. Who did he score his first Sunderland goal against?

123. With which club did McGeady first play for Simon Grayson?

124. In which year did he score on his senior debut for Celtic?

125. Who was the future Sunderland manager he played for at Celtic?

126. In which season was he SFPA Player and Young Player of the Year?

127. Glasgow born, he has over 90 caps for which country?

128. Which Russian club did he play for?

129. Who were his first English club?

130. Which club did his dad play in the top-flight for in 1975-76?

2014 CAPITAL ONE CUP

131. Who did Sunderland play in the 2014 Capital One Cup final?

132. Which Sunderland player's birthday was the final played on?

133. Who scored for Sunderland?

134. How long had been played when Sunderland went ahead?

135. Who equalised?

136. After Samir Nasri put Sunderland behind, who completed the scoring with a last-minute goal?

137. Which member of the Sunderland side had played in the previous season's final?

138. Who was the manager of Manchester United when Sunderland beat them at the semi-final stage?

139. Which team had Sunderland knocked out of the Capital One Cup and would also eliminate from the FA Cup in the same season?

140. Which club led 2-0 at Sunderland with 13 minutes to go in the first game of the cup run?

QUIZ 15
BRENDAN GALLOWAY

141. In 2017-18, Galloway was on a season-long loan from which club?

142. Which of the clubs Sunderland knocked out of the 2013-14 Capital One Cup was Brendan with at the time?

143. He made his Premier League debut at West Ham in May of which year?

144. What was the score when he first played against Sunderland in November 2015?

145. Who did he make three Premier League appearances on loan to in 2016-17?

146. Who was the European Cup-winning full-back who called Brendan up to play for England Under-17s?

147. Who did Brendan make his Sunderland debut against?

148. Which squad number was he given at the Stadium of Light?

149. Prior to joining Sunderland, in which year had his last Premier League appearance for Everton been?

150. Why should he fascinate compilers of SAFC A to Z guides?

QUIZ 16
JOHN O'SHEA

151.   Which manager signed O'Shea for Sunderland?

152.   Who did John score his first goal for Sunderland against?

153.   As of the beginning of the 2017-18 season, how many men had played more for the Republic of Ireland than John?

154.   As of the beginning of 2017-18, John was one of how many of the Republic of Ireland's top eight appearance-makers to have played for Sunderland?

155.   How did he mark winning his 100th cap away to World Champions Germany?

156.   How many times did he win the Premier League with Manchester United?

157.   Other than Sunderland and Manchester United which other English club has he played for?

158.   Which overseas club has he played for?

159.   In which year did O'Shea join Sunderland?

160.   Asamoah Gyan and which defender played their last games for Sunderland on John's debut?

NIALL QUINN

161. In which year did Niall score in a game that relegated Sunderland?

162. Who did he play against in Sunderland's first-ever Premier League game?

163. Who did he score twice against in Sunderland's first-ever Premier League win?

164. Who did he score against for the first-ever goal at the Stadium of Light?

165. Who were Sunderland playing when Niall scored the Stadium of Light's first hat-trick?

166. Who were Sunderland playing when he went in goal after scoring the only goal of the game?

167. Who were Manchester City playing when he saved a penalty after scoring in a top-flight game?

168. Who were the Republic of Ireland playing when he scored in the 1990 World Cup finals?

169. Who did Sunderland beat in his last match as Sunderland manager?

170. How many people have scored more goals at the Stadium of Light than Niall?

SIMON GRAYSON

171. What connection did Simon have to Sunderland's first-ever Premier League game?

172. How many times was Grayson on the losing side against Sunderland in eight appearances?

173. Which former Sunderland defender was a teammate of Grayson's when he made his league debut for Leeds?

174. Which North East team were the beaten finalists when he won the League Cup in 1997?

175. Who was he playing for when he completed his playing career in 2005?

176. Who were the first club he managed?

177. How many different clubs has Grayson led to promotion?

178. How many Manager of the Month awards had Simon won prior to coming to Sunderland, four, five or six?

179. Which former Sunderland midfielder did he replace as manager of Huddersfield?

180. Who scored the only goal of the game in his first competitive win as Sunderland manager?

181. What is the record number of successive wins in derby games between Sunderland and Newcastle?

182. To the start of the 2017-18 season, how long was Sunderland's unbeaten run in games against Newcastle United?

183. Who scored a hat-trick against Newcastle in 1979?

184. In the same game the hat-trick hero laid Sunderland's other goal on a plate for which teammate?

185. Who scored the goals in the 1990 Play-Off meeting between Sunderland and Newcastle?

186. Which goalkeeper saved a penalty from Alan Shearer at St. James' Park in 2000?

187. When Kevin Phillips became the first Englishman to win the European Golden Shoe as the continent's top scorer, what percentage of his goals had been scored against Newcastle?

188. Who scored Sunderland's goal in the 1-1 draw at Newcastle in March 2016?

189. In what year did Kieran Richardson score the winner in the Wear-Tyne derby?

190. What is the record score in Sunderland v Newcastle derbies?

DEBUTS

191. Which player's debut at Barnsley in 1995 was his only appearance as Sunderland were fined - and could have been docked points - for not registering him properly?

192. Who was the brother of a 1973 cup winner whose only appearance for Sunderland in that cup-winning season was his solitary game for the club?

193. Who scored four goals on his debut against Portsmouth in 1947?

194. How many goals did Sunderland concede on Player of the Century Charlie Hurley's debut in 1957?

195. Who else debuted on the same day as King Charlie?

196. Who scored the only goal of the game on his debut at Bolton in August 2009?

197. Who scored the winner at Spurs on his debut in August 2008?

198. Who was Britain's costliest goalkeeper who kept a clean sheet against Spurs in August 2007?

199. Who became Sunderland's youngest Premier League player when he debuted against Manchester United on Boxing Day 2007?

200. Who debuted in goal against Leicester in 1964 when he was only 15?

NICK SUMMERBEE

201. How many of Summerbee's 108 Sunderland games were starts?

202. Which top scorer in a promotion side went to Manchester City in exchange for Nick?

203. What was the first name of Nick's dad who had starred for Manchester City and England?

204. Which other relation of Nick had played over 150 league games?

205. Who did Summerbee score against in a 4-1 away win on his debut in 1997?

206. Who did Summerbee score against at Wembley for Sunderland?

207. With which club did he begin his career?

208. Who did he play for after leaving Sunderland?

209. After leaving Sunderland, which club did he play most games for?

210. Did he play for England at Under-21 or 'B' level?

JOHNNY CROSSAN

211. How many league goals did Crossan score when he was top-scorer in Sunderland's first-ever promotion season?

212. How many goals did he score as Sunderland won 6-2 on his debut in 1962?

213. Who had he been playing for when he played in a European Cup semi-final before joining Sunderland?

214. In total, Johnny scored 48 goals for Sunderland. Did he play over or under 100 games?

215. Who were the cup holders he scored twice against away from home in the 1964 FA Cup quarter-final?

216. Who did he captain to promotion in 1966?

217. Which North East team paid a club record fee for him in 1967?

218. Of the dozen Northern Ireland caps won while with Sunderland, in how many did he have club-mate Martin Harvey as a teammate, 10,11 or 12?

219. Who were the two-time former World Champions Johnny scored twice against towards the end of Sunderland's promotion season?

220. In all competitions for club and country, how many goals did Crossan score in the 1963-64 promotion season?

221. Willie Watson played for England at football and which other sport?

222. He is one of how many men who are double-internationals in these sports?

223. How many of the double-internationals won as many combined caps in the two sports as Watson?

224. Who were England playing when Willie won one of his football caps at Roker Park?

225. Who had his dad won three league titles with in successive years?

226. His brother Albert captained Oldham and also played for which club?

227. Which English club did he go to become player/manager of?

228. Which other English club did he manage?

229. In which overseas country did he manage?

230. In which year's World Cup was he a travelling reserve?

231. Who were Sunderland playing when Stan scored in the game that clinched promotion in 1980?

232. Who were Sunderland playing when Stan scored in the game that ensured Sunderland stayed up?

233. Who were Sunderland playing when Stan scored four in a game?

234. In which season did Stan score the winner at home to Newcastle having earlier scored at St. James' Park?

235. Which manager paid a club record fee of £300,000 for him in November 1979?

236. Who was signed a month later to make Stan's time as SAFC record-signing short-lived?

237. Which World Cup winner predicted Cummins would become the game's first £1m player when he was his manager at Middlesbrough?

238. Which London club did Stan play for between his two spells at Sunderland?

239. Stan later settled in the USA, which was the American club he joined on loan from Sunderland?

240. Stan had been discovered by a scout called Ray Grant. Which legendary player, who like Stan played for Middlesbrough and Sunderland, had Grant also unearthed?

DICKIE DAVIS

241. How many league goals did Dickie Davis score to become top scorer in the top flight?

242. In which season did he achieve this distinction?

243. Why did Dickie have to wait seven years for his Sunderland debut?

244. Despite his goals, Davis was moved to inside-forward the following season, after Sunderland paid a national record-fee to sign which centre-forward?

245. Davis played 154 games for the club, did he score 75, 80 or 85 goals?

246. Which other North East club did Dickie move onto in 1954?

247. Birmingham born, which of his home city clubs did he play for as a 'Guest' during World War Two?

248. How many of Sunderland's trio of hat-tricks in his national top-scoring season did Dickie score?

249. In December 1950, Davis and the big-money buy signed to replace him, each scored twice at the Baseball Ground against Derby, but Sunderland still lost. What was the score?

250. After Davis, who was the next Sunderland player to be the top-flight's top scorer?

251. Which manager signed Bally?

252. Who was he bought from?

253. Which two England stars, fresh from Italia 90, did he face on his debut?

254. How many times did he play at Wembley for Sunderland?

255. In which season was his brilliant headed goal against Chelsea in a 3-0 Premier League win?

256. Who did he score against in the Play-Offs?

257. Which club rejected him as a youngster?

258. After leaving Sunderland, which two clubs did he play for?

259. Which future England captain did Kevin bring through at Under-18 level and beyond?

260. When Sunderland reached the Capital One Cup final in 2013-14, which team were knocked out while Kevin was acting as caretaker-manager?

COLIN TODD

261. At which of the grounds that would later be his home-club ground did Colin win his first England Under-23 cap while a Sunderland player?

262. In which year did he play in the FA Youth Cup final for Sunderland against Arsenal?

263. At which London ground did he make his first-team debut less than two months after England won the World Cup in 1966?

264. What happened in the one game Colin missed in 1968-69?

265. What was the record fee for a defender, paid for him when he was sold in February 1971?

266. Who was the former Sunderland youth team manager who bought him for Derby?

267. How many league titles did Todd win with the Rams?

268. Which individual award did he win in 1975?

269. He played 668 club games. Did he manage in more or fewer games than he played?

270. How many full England caps did he win?

JOHNNY COCHRANE

271. What is Johnny Cochrane's unique achievement as Sunderland manager?

272. What did he lead Sunderland to in 1931, 1937 and 1938?

273. In which season were Sunderland league runners-up under Cochrane?

274. In which season did Cochrane lead Sunderland to a sixth league title?

275. In which season did Cochrane lead Sunderland to a first FA Cup triumph?

276. Who did Sunderland beat when under Cochrane, Sunderland won the Charity Shield?

277. Which club had he played for in Scotland before becoming their secretary?

278. After Sunderland he managed which other club, but just for 14 days?

279. Which team had he managed to their first Scottish Cup success?

280. In which year did Cochrane become Sunderland manager?

THOMAS SORENSEN

281. What was the record number of clean-sheets Sorensen kept in 1998-99?

282. Who was his deputy who kept another clean-sheet in the one game he played that season?

283. Which French goalkeeper was Sorensen signed to replace?

284. Which Sunderland goalkeeper did Peter Reid send to assess Sorensen before signing him?

285. Who did Thomas help Sunderland win a penalty shoot-out against in his first season?

286. Who did he play against in a cup semi-final for Sunderland?

287. Who gave away the penalty when Sorensen saved from Alan Shearer at St. James' Park?

288. In which year was Tommy North East Football Writers' Association Player of the Year?

289. While with Sunderland he played at the 2002 World Cup keeping a clean-sheet against which country?

290. In whose Testimonial did Thomas play as a striker at the Stadium of Light?

JORDAN PICKFORD

291. How old was Jordan when he started training with Sunderland?

292. When he was sold by his first club, which club had he made most league appearances for?

293. How many clubs did Pickford go on loan to while with Sunderland?

294. Who was his manager in the last of those loans?

295. With which club did he set a club record for consecutive clean-sheets?

296. Pickford became the first Sunderland goalkeeper since who, to be a sub for England?

297. Had Pickford stayed with the club until he won a first full cap, which goalkeeper would he have emulated as winning a full England cap while with Sunderland?

298. Name the Arsenal player who scored the first goal Pickford conceded on his Sunderland debut?

299. How many goals did Jordan concede in his two games against Everton in his final season with Sunderland?

300. In which competition did he make his debut for Everton?

TONY TOWERS

301. Who was Tony signed from?

302. What were the two noteworthy things he had done against Sunderland during the 1973 FA Cup run?

303. In which year had he won the European Cup-Winners' Cup while a teenager?

304. Who had he played against at Wembley in the League Cup final only a fortnight before signing for Sunderland?

305. Which two members of the 1973 FA Cup-winning team went in the opposite direction to Tony as part of his transfer deal?

306. How many goals did penalty-taking midfielder Towers get in the 1975-76 promotion season?

307. Who was the Chairman of Newcastle United and President of the Football League who handed the 1976 Division Two Championship trophy to Tony?

308. How many England caps did Towers win while with Sunderland?

309. Which Sunderland manager sold Tony to Birmingham City?

310. Who was the former Sunderland FA Cup winner and teammate, Tony made the final appearances of his career for at Rochdale?

311. The quickest man to 50 goals for Sunderland took 52 games. He was a member of the Team of All The Talents and the half-brother of a future manager. Name him.

312. The second quickest took 55 games in the 1920s and holds Sunderland's seasonal scoring record. Who is it?

313. It took this man 57 games, but he was even more successful as a manager, winning the European Cup twice with Nottingham Forest. Who is it?

314. Another member of 'the Talents,' this man also became the first of only four men in history to score five goals in a game for the club. Who is it?

315. Taking 73 games, who is this super-striker who was the first Englishman to win the European Golden Shoe?

316. Nicknamed Cannonball or Legs, who is this fifties forward who hit his first 50 goals in 77 games?

317. Nicknamed 'Blood', who is this member of 'the Talents' who scored 50 times in his first 83 games?

318. Who is the record signing Wales international who took 85 games to score 50 in the fifties?

319. 50 in 87 games included five in one game against Norwich for this Scottish striker who played in the sixties. Name him.

320. Who is this member of the 'G-Force' who came from York City and reached 50 goals in 88 games?

JULIO ARCA

321. Which country is Julio from?

322. Which other English league club did he play for after he left Sunderland?

323. Which club did Julio play at Wembley for in 2017?

324. Who did Julio score against on his Sunderland debut, Watford, West Brom or West Ham?

325. Which other South American made his debut for Sunderland in the same game as Arca - Nicolas Medina, Emerson Thome or Marcos Di Guiseppe?

326. In what year did Julio play his last game for Sunderland, 2004, 2005 or 2006?

327. When Julio won the FIFA Under-20 World Cup in 2001, which African nation were defeated in the final?

328. What is the name of the club Sunderland signed Arca from?

329. Which English ground did Peter Reid first spot Julio at?

330. When Julio scored his never-to-be-forgotten goal at Bradford in 2003 when he dribbled three-quarters of the pitch before chipping the 'keeper, who was in goal for the Bantams?

331. Who was the young Scot bought from St. Johnstone for £355,000 in 1981?

332. Who did Peter Reid pay Manchester City £1.3m for as the club's first Premier League season was about to start?

333. Who was the midfielder, with shocking taste in tee-shirts, bought for £2.5m from Newcastle in 1997?

334. Who was the man Roy Keane made Britain's costliest goalkeeper when paying £9m to Hearts in 2007?

335. With add-ons, who is this striker who cost £16.5m from Spurs in 2009?

336. Who was Sunderland's first £100,000 player signed as a centre-forward in 1970, but later better at centre-half?

337. Who was Sunderland's first £200,000 player, signed from Leicester City by Bob Stokoe in 1976?

338. Who was this maverick signed for a national record for £20,050 from Newcastle United in 1948?

339. Later the world's first £1,000 player when sold to Middlesbrough, who was this player Sunderland paid a national record of £520 to sign from Sheffield United in 1904?

340. Name the £3.75m midfielder bought from Valencia in 1999.

341. Which striker scored for England at Wembley in 2016-17 while on Sunderland's books?

342. Who won his only cap against Australia in 1983?

343. Who was the only Sunderland player capped by England during the 1960s?

344. Who won his only cap against Holland at Wembley in 2012?

345. Later to captain his country, who won his first cap against France at Wembley in 2010 while still with his first club Sunderland?

346. Who won his only cap in Sven-Goran Eriksson's first match as England manager against Spain in 2001?

347. Who has scored most goals for England while on Sunderland's books?

348. Who has won most caps for England while on Sunderland's books?

349. The first man capped by England while with the club was for a match played in Sunderland against Wales in 1891. Who was it?

350. Who was the midfielder who was so good, he played for England at both football and cricket?

1936 CHAMPIONS

351. When Sunderland became champions in 1936, how many titles did it mean the club had won?

352. At that point, how many clubs had won it more?

353. The relegation of Aston Villa and Blackburn Rovers in the same season meant what for Sunderland?

354. Who was Sunderland's manager?

355. Which two players scored 31 goals each?

356. How many teams in the top half of the table conceded more goals than Sunderland?

357. Did Sunderland score over or under 100 goals?

358. Who had won the title for the three previous seasons in a row?

359. Who were the runners-up to Sunderland in 1936?

360. Who was the Sunderland goalkeeper who tragically lost his life after playing in the first 28 games of the season?

1937 FA CUP WINNERS

361. Who did Sunderland beat in the final?

362. What was the score?

363. Which very famous future Liverpool manager was playing for the opposition?

364. Who was Sunderland's captain?

365. Who scored Sunderland's first goal?

366. Who scored Sunderland's last goal?

367. Which third division team had been beaten in the semi-final?

368. Which Scottish international had scored both goals in the semi-final?

369. Which team had taken Sunderland to two replays to beat them in the quarter-final?

370. As cup holders, who did Sunderland face in the following season's Charity Shield?

THE 2017-18 SEASON

371. Who was appointed manager at the start of the season?

372. Who was the first game against?

373. Who scored Sunderland's first goal of the season?

374. Who was Sunderland's first win in any competition against?

375. Who scored his first two goals for the club in the space of three games in August?

376. Whose first goal for the club was the winner in the Carabao Cup game at Carlisle?

377. Which former Sunderland reserve player saw his team inflict a 3-0 defeat on the Lads in August?

378. Which former Sunderland player returned to score a late winner at the Stadium of Light for Nottingham Forest?

379. When Sunderland played Everton in the Carabao Cup, what was worn as the logo on the shirts?

380. Which former Sunderland player scored in the defeat at Ipswich?

JONNY WILLIAMS

381. Johnny joined on a season-long loan in 2017-18, from which London club?

382. Which international team does he play for?

383. Which award did he win in 2012-13?

384. Which club did he go on loan to four times?

385. Which former Sunderland manager did he play for in all of those loans?

386. Of the clubs he had played on loan for, which was the first he played against, after coming to Sunderland?

387. Who were the third club he played for on loan?

388. Which squad number was he given at Sunderland?

389. Who did he make his Sunderland debut against?

390. At which major tournament was he part of the Wales squad?

LEWIS GRABBAN

391. Which London club did Grabban begin his career with?

392. Which rival London club bought him for £150,000 in 2008?

393. After playing for Brentford, which former Bees boss then took him to Rotherham?

394. Which on-the-up south coast club paid £300,000 for Lewis in 2012?

395. Who was he then sold to for £3m?

396. Which of his former clubs then bought him back for a fee believed to be around £6m?

397. Who did he join on loan and play for in a Play-Off final against Huddersfield?

398. Which of his former clubs did he score twice against for Sunderland in August?

399. Which Scottish team has Grabban played for?

400. Which squad number was he given when he arrived at Sunderland.

QUIZ 41
JAMES VAUGHAN

401. Who did he score his first Sunderland goal against?

402. Which manager gave James his league debut for Everton?

403. In scoring his first Premier League goal at the age of 16 years and 271 days, whose record did he take as the Premier League's youngest scorer?

404. That goal also made him Everton's youngest scorer. Whose place did he take in the record books?

405. Who had been Everton's youngest player before Vaughan's debut?

406. What is the highest level Vaughan represented England at?

407. Which other country is he eligible for selection for?

408. Who were the first club James went on loan to?

409. Which club did he go on loan to under Simon Grayson, subsequently signing for him?

410. How many goals did he score for Bury in 2016-17, 20, 24 or 27?

QUIZ 42
VIC HALOM

411.   What number did Halom wear in the 1973 FA Cup final?

412.   His first goal in the cup run was a screamer in the game voted the best-ever at Roker Park. Who was it against?

413.   Who did Vic score against in the FA Cup semi-final?

414.   Which top team did he score a hat-trick against in the following season's League Cup?

415.   Sunderland's first game in Europe took Halom to the country his father was from, which country was that?

416.   As well as the FA Cup, which other trophy did Vic win at Sunderland?

417.   At which club was he player/coach to Ian Porterfield?

418.   During the cup-winning season, he scored against Sunderland when still playing for which club?

419.   Which very famous comedian was a director of that club and wrote to congratulate Vic on winning the FA Cup with Sunderland?

420.   He later stood for Parliament in Sunderland, for which Party?

DAVID HALLIDAY

421. David Halliday holds Sunderland's scoring record of most goals in a season, how many did he score, 40, 43 or 45?

422. In which season did he manage this, 1927-28, 1928-29 or 1929-30?

423. How many hat-tricks did he score in his record season?

424. How many Sunderland forwards have ever scored as many goals in a season as Halliday did in his poorest season at the club?

425. Born in Dumfries, how many caps did he win for Scotland?

426. When he signed for Sunderland in 1925, how many games did it take him to reach ten goals?

427. Which Scottish club did Sunderland buy him from?

428. Who did Sunderland sell him to in 1929?

429. Who did he move on to a year later?

430. What role did he play in Sunderland's first-ever relegation some three decades after he played for the club?

NORTHERN IRELAND INTERNATIONALS

431. Which Northern Ireland international did David Moyes buy from Manchester United in 2016?

432. Which Northern Ireland international defender did Sunderland have on loan from Manchester United a decade earlier?

433. What was the surname of Sunderland's Northern Ireland international whose first name was English?

434. Which winger was on Sunderland's books when he played at the 1958 World Cup with Northern Ireland? He later managed them in the 1982 World Cup finals.

435. Who was the forward capped twice in the early sixties?

436. Who was the Sunderland player who won 34 Northern Ireland caps between 1961 and 1971?

437. Who were the three Sunderland players chosen for the November 1964 games against Switzerland and Scotland?

438. Which of that trio had been sold to Sunderland by Jock Stein when he was manager of Hibs?

439. Which 1990s forward scored five times in the 13 games he played while with Sunderland?

440. Which 2000s left-back scored on his Northern Ireland debut, but never scored in over 200 games for Sunderland?

WALES INTERNATIONALS

441. Which two Wales internationals did Sunderland have in their side in the early part of the 2017-18 season?

442. Which Wales international scored for Sunderland in the 3-0 win at Newcastle under Paolo Di Canio?

443. Which midfielder won his first cap as a Sunderland player against England in a 2004 World Cup qualifying game at Old Trafford, before going on to manage in Canada?

444. Which winger won ten caps while with Sunderland and was part of the Sunderland and Reading squads which achieved 105 and 106 points in promotion campaigns?

445. Which centre-back scored three times for Wales in the 17 times he played for them while with Sunderland in the mid-1990s?

446. Who was the winger who won eight Wales caps while at Sunderland and was later assistant to Brendan Rodgers at Swansea and Liverpool?

447. Which Welsh winger scored the winning goal for Burnley against Sunderland at Roker Park in a 1970 youth tournament and won one of his 57 caps for Wales against England at Wembley in 1983 while with Sunderland?

448. Who left reigning champions Arsenal to sign for Sunderland in 1953, going on to win nine of his 21 caps while with Sunderland?

449. Which fifties forward scored 12 goals - including two against England at Roker Park - in 13 internationals while with Sunderland?

450. Who was the legendary and eccentric goalkeeper who won nine caps while with Sunderland, but was killed in the First World War?

LEN ASHURST

451. Which club appearances record does Len hold?

452. Which position did he play?

453. What was his self-penned autobiography called?

454. As manager in which season did he lead Sunderland to Wembley in the League Cup final, but also see the team relegated?

455. Len was one of how many ever-presents in the 1963-64 promotion season?

456. What was the nickname his teammates gave to him?

457. Who were the other two debutants on the day he debuted? Between the trio, they would total over 1,100 appearances for the club.

458. How many games did Len play for Sunderland?

459. Who did he play for on his first visit to Roker Park?

460. Which club did he manage to the quarter-finals of the European Cup-Winners' Cup?

QUIZ 47
GEORGE HERD

461. Which international team did George represent?

462. Inside-right Herd scored exactly one goal per three games played in 1963-64 in the league and FA Cup. How many goals did he score, 15, 16 or 17?

463. Herd made his debut against Liverpool in the last game of 1960-61. What happened to near namesake and fellow debutant Robert Hird?

464. Sunderland signed Herd from Clyde, which trophy had he won with them in 1958?

465. Which other North East club did Herd complete his playing days with?

466. With which of his 1964 promotion winning teammates did George later coach the Sunderland youth team?

467. Did George play 218, 318 or 418 games for Sunderland?

468. In which year did George play his final game for Sunderland?

469. Which overseas country did George coach in?

470. Which local non-league team was George still coaching well into his seventies?

JORDAN HENDERSON

471. Jordan Henderson's debut for Sunderland was at the same London club as George Herd's last. Where?

472. At which Scottish club did Jordan first appear at first-team level in a Testimonial for Alex Lawrie?

473. Who did Jordan score against in the 2008 FA Youth Cup semi-final?

474. Roy Keane gave Jordan his debut, but which manager gave him his first start - against the same team he had debuted against nine months earlier?

475. Jordan's first Premier League goal was on the same ground as his youth cup semi-final strike, what was the score on the day he first scored in the Premier League?

476. Who did he score twice against in his third-last home game before being transferred?

477. In which year was he sold to Liverpool?

478. Which club did he play for on loan while with Sunderland?

479. Up to the end of September 2017, how many times had Henderson captained England?

480. Who were England playing when Jordan was capped at the Stadium of Light?

STEPHANE SESSEGNON

481. Who did Sunderland sign Sessegnon from?

482. Which of his seven clubs had he played most games for, as of September 2017?

483. Who was Sunderland's Head Coach when Stephane scored in a 3-0 win at Newcastle?

484. Who did Sunderland sell Sessegnon to?

485. Who did he score against on his debut for his new club?

486. In which season was he Player of the Year at Sunderland?

487. During that season how many managers did he play for at Sunderland - including caretakers?

488. According to the fans' chant, which two players had God taken to produce Stephane Sessegnon?

489. Which French side did he sign for in September 2016?

490. Which international side does he play for?

THE 1949-50 SEASON

491. How many points were Sunderland behind the champions in 1949-50?

492. What position did the Lads finish?

493. Who won the league on goal average?

494. How many times had Sunderland lost against teams in the top six?

495. Which team, who were relegated, won at Roker Park four games from the end of the season to, in effect, cost Sunderland a seventh league title?

496. Who was Sunderland's top scorer who was also top scorer in the country?

497. Who was Sunderland's manager?

498. Sunderland's record league crowd was established this season against Newcastle, was it 58,004, 68,004 or 78,004?

499. Who was the full-back who was ever-present during this season?

500. Who were the two wingers who were also ever-present?

501. In which decade were Sunderland known as 'The Bank of England Team'?

502. In which season of the decade did they come closest to success in the league?

503. Who was the centre-forward Sunderland broke the transfer record to buy in October 1950 when they already had the league's top scorer from the previous season?

504. Who was the international winger bought in the same month to supply the centre-forward's ammunition?

505. Sunderland would have met Newcastle in the FA Cup final had they not lost to which club in the 1955 semi-final?

506. Sunderland beat Newcastle away in the 1956 FA Cup quarter-final only to lose to which team in the semi-final?

507. Which long-serving manager departed in 1957?

508. Directors and players were banned as a result of what?

509. What did 'The Bank of England Team' win?

510. What record did Sunderland lose having invested in 'The Bank of England Team'?

TREVOR FORD

511. How many goals did Ford score for Sunderland in his 117 games, 50, 60 or 70?

512. Who did Sunderland buy him from for a national record of £29,500?

513. He famously scored a hat-trick and dislodged a goal-post on his home debut. Who were Sunderland playing?

514. For Wales, how many goals did he score in his 38 games, 22, 23 or 24?

515. Which Dutch club did he play for?

516. Why was he playing on the continent?

517. Which future Sunderland manager signed him for the Dutch club?

518. Always determined, Trevor once stayed on the pitch with a broken ankle in a cup replay at Scunthorpe. What did he contribute?

519. Until Ian Rush came along, who did Ford share the Wales goal-scoring record with?

520. Which legendary West Indian cricketer hit six sixes in an over when Ford was playing for Glamorgan as 12th man?

521. In Shack's autobiography he famously left a blank page under a chapter heading. What was the blank chapter called?

522. How long did Shack have to wait for another cap after scoring a mesmerising goal against reigning World Champions West Germany at Wembley?

523. Which club famously rejected Shack as a youngster?

524. Which club did he make his name with before joining Newcastle United?

525. How many goals did he score on his debut for Newcastle?

526. When Sunderland signed him, why was the fee £20,050?

527. What was the odd fee Newcastle had reportedly paid for him?

528. How many goals did he score for Sunderland?

529. Known simply as Shack, what was the nickname his autobiography was also given?

530. He retired after one game under which manager at Sunderland?

531. Who is Sunderland's youngest-ever player?

532. He was so many years and 185 days when he debuted in 1964. How many years?

533. Who is Sunderland's youngest-ever goalscorer?

534. He was so many years and 103 days when he was a debut-scorer against Preston in 1971. How many years?

535. Who had been Sunderland's youngest-ever player when he debuted against Ipswich in 1958?

536. Which centre-half was only 16 when he debuted at Orient in 1978?

537. Which centre-forward was only 16 when he debuted against Scunthorpe in 1960?

538. Which goalkeeper was only 39 days past his 17th birthday when he debuted in 1930, only to pass away less than six years later?

539. Who became Sunderland's youngest Premier League player when he debuted against Manchester United in 2007?

540. Who took his record when he debuted against Middlesbrough in 2016?

OLDEST PLAYERS

541. At 39 years and 76 days, who is Sunderland's oldest player?

542. At 38 years and 183 days, who is Sunderland's oldest scorer?

543. At 37 years and 58 days, who became Sunderland's eldest debutant when he played against Reading in 2005?

544. Who had become Sunderland's eldest debutant when he also debuted against Reading the previous year when he was 37 years and 21 days?

545. Who became Sunderland's third oldest ever goalscorer when he scored his only goal for Sunderland in the final league game at Roker Park when he was 36 and 140 days?

546. Kevin Ball became Sunderland's oldest scorer in the League Cup when he scored at the age of 34 and 334 days in 1999, against who?

547. Who is Sunderland's oldest Premier League player, having been 37 years and 280 days when he played his final game at Manchester City in August 2000?

548. Which former Manchester United star signed off his career as Sunderland's fifth oldest player at the age of 37 and 159 days, against Manchester United in 2009?

549. Who is the oldest former-Newcastle player to play for Sunderland? He was 40 days past his 36th birthday when he played his final game in 2007.

550. Who became the oldest goalkeeper to debut for Sunderland when he played in the club's first-ever Premier League game?

CHARLIE BUCHAN

551. Charlie is Sunderland's leading league goal-scorer. Did he score 200, 209 or 228 league goals?

552. In league and cup, Buchan played 411 games for Sunderland. In total did he score 211, 220 or 222 goals?

553. How many goals did he score in the six internationals he played while on Sunderland's books, 0, 2 or 4?

554. He was the first man to score five goals in a league game for Sunderland. Who against?

555. In which year was he an FA Cup finalist for a club other than Sunderland?

556. In which season was he top scorer as Sunderland won the league title?

557. In which year's FA Cup final did he play for Sunderland?

558. What feat did he achieve with 30 league goals when Sunderland were league runners-up in 1922-23?

559. Who was he transferred to?

560. After his playing days were over, which best-selling football magazine did he establish?

RAICH CARTER

561. What was Raich's full name?

562. With which league club had he been on trial before joining Sunderland?

563. Playing against England for 'The Rest' at Roker Park in 1934, how many goals did he score as he inspired 'The Rest' to a 7-1 win?

564. Raich scored his first goal in a 7-4 win over Bolton Wanderers on his home debut. In which season was that?

565. When Sunderland won the league in 1935-36, who was Raich joint top-scorer with?

566. How many goals did they each score in the championship-winning season?

567. In how many seasons was Carter Sunderland's outright top scorer, one, two or three?

568. Was his goal in the 1937 FA Cup final Sunderland's first, second or third?

569. Who was he playing against Sunderland for in the first league match after the Second World War?

570. He was the only man to achieve which particular feat before and after the war?

MICHAEL GRAY

571. How many of these players made more appearances for Sunderland than Michael: Gordon Armstrong, Charlie Hurley, Bobby Gurney and Kevin Ball?

572. Who were Sunderland playing when Michael marked his home debut with a first-minute goal at the Fulwell End?

573. In which season did Michael make his debut?

574. What were the first names of the other two Grays to play for Sunderland while Michael was at the club?

575. Michael was one of two ever-presents in the side that won Division One in 1995-96. Which full-back was the other?

576. In which season did he score in the derby at St. James' Park?

577. Against which Premier League team had Michael had a penalty saved, before his infamous Wembley penalty against Charlton?

578. How many full England caps did he go on to win?

579. With which Scottish winger did Gray form a magic left-wing partnership at the Stadium of Light?

580. Which club did Michael go on loan to while with Sunderland?

GORDON ARMSTRONG

581. Gordon holds the record for making more appearances in a single season than any other player. How many games did he play in that record-breaking season, 57, 58 or 59?

582. Which season was it?

583. How many players have made more appearances for Sunderland than Gordon, six, 16 or 26?

584. Only one of those appearances saw him play at centre-back. Was it his debut or final appearance?

585. In which season did Tyneside-born Armstrong score against Newcastle?

586. On the occasion of his famous last-minute winner in the 1992 FA Cup quarter-final replay with Chelsea, who had scored Sunderland's other goal in the game?

587. Which medal did Gordon win at Sunderland?

588. He played for Northampton and which other club on loan from Sunderland?

589. With who did he play against Sunderland in the opening season at the Stadium of Light?

590. Can you name his brother who played for Reading and Sheffield United?

PLAYED ONCE

591. England international who scored against Newcastle in the 1976 League Cup final. Only Sunderland appearance was at Swindon in 1989.

592. Scotland international, brother of 1973 cup winner. Only game v Millwall in 1973.

593. Scot, subbed in a 4-0 win over Ipswich in 1989. Former York player.

594. Costly Argentinian who played 120 minutes in his only match against Bolton in 2003.

595. Scored against England at Euro 92 for Sweden five years before his only Sunderland match at Villa.

596. His only appearance saw him come on for his brother at Leeds in 1989.

597. 1967 Youth Cup winner who played at Everton in 1968 and was later a teammate of George Best at Dunstable.

598. Brazilian player signed from Peruvian club. Only game v Walsall in 1999. Walsall then signed him and he only played once for them too.

599. One appearance at Manchester City in 2003. The brother of long standing Academy coach Elliott who in 2017 was Under-23 coach.

600. His one appearance at Barnsley in 1995 saw Sunderland fined as he wasn't properly registered.

QUIZ 61
JIM MONTGOMERY

601. Sunderland's highest appearance-maker with 627. Other than Jim, how many players have reached 500 games for the club?

602. In which year did Monty make his debut in a League Cup tie with Walsall?

603. Who did Sunderland beat on Monty's league debut in February 1962?

604. How many games did Monty miss in his first two full seasons of 1962-63 and 1963-64?

605. When injured in 1964-65, which Scottish 'keeper was signed with Jim having to compete with him for the first-team shirt?

606. Having re-established himself as number one, how many games did Monty miss in the five seasons starting in 1966-67, none, two or four?

607. Monty famously kept a clean-sheet in the 1973 FA Cup final at Wembley. When had been his previous FA Cup cleansheet away from Roker Park?

608. He later signed for which manager who had scored a hat-trick on Jim's Sunderland debut against Walsall?

609. With which club did he win a European Cup-Winners' medal as back-up 'keeper to Peter Shilton?

610. How old was Monty when he left Sunderland as a player?

2006-07 PROMOTION

611. Who began the season as manager?

612. Who completed the season as manager?

613. Who was the top scorer?

614. Who was the Player of the Year?

615. How many points were taken from the first four games?

616. In which month did Sunderland first enter an automatic promotion position?

617. Who were beaten in the last home game when Carlos Edwards' great late goal made promotion almost certain?

618. Who beat eventual third-placed side Derby County to mathematically confirm Sunderland's promotion?

619. Who did Sunderland beat 5-0 away in the final game of the season?

620. Against who did runners-up Birmingham slip-up against on the final day to allow Sunderland to take the title?

QUIZ 63
BRIAN CLOUGH

621. Brian Clough played 74 games for Sunderland, how many goals did he score, 43, 53 or 63?

622. Who was he injured against on Boxing Day 1962, in the game that effectively ended his playing days?

623. Who was the opposition centre-half that day?

624. The injury came in Clough's 28th appearance of the season. How many goals had he scored in that campaign, 20, 24 or 28?

625. Who had Sunderland signed Brian from?

626. When Clough attempted a comeback 21 months later he managed three games. He scored once against which team he would later go on to manage?

627. After coaching Sunderland youths, who were the first Football League club Clough managed?

628. Which was the first club he managed to the league title?

629. Which was the club with which he won the League title and the European Cup twice?

630. Who was the member of the Roker Park office staff who Clough appointed as the League's youngest secretary at Derby and who in 2017 is secretary of the Sunderland Senior Supporters' Association?

THE FIRST PROMOTION SEASON

631. Who was promotion clinched against?

632. Which already relegated team were played in the last match of the season?

633. Who won the division as Sunderland went up with them?

634. How many ever-presents did Sunderland have in their first promotion campaign?

635. Who was Sunderland's captain?

636. Who was top scorer?

637. Who were the reigning top-flight champions Sunderland knocked out of the FA Cup in the fifth round?

638. Who were the FA Cup holders Sunderland took to two replays in the quarter-final?

639. Who was the manager?

640. Which season was it?

THE SECOND PROMOTION SEASON

641. In which season were Sunderland promoted for a second time?

642. Who was the manager?

643. How many of the 1973 FA Cup winning team played in the promotion season?

644. What round of the FA Cup did the promotion team reach?

645. Who were runners-up to Sunderland?

646. Who was Sunderland's top-scorer?

647. Who made his debut during the season and would go on to become the club's post-war record goal-scorer? A record he held until Kevin Phillips came along.

648. Other than the FA Cup and League Cup, which other cup competition did Sunderland play in, beating Newcastle?

649. Who was the centre-half who debuted on the opening day and was excellent in the first three-quarters of the campaign before being injured?

650. Which future Sunderland manager scored for Bolton at Roker Park on the day promotion was confirmed?

651. In which month of 1966 did Roker Park stage World Cup games?

652. How many World Cup finals games did Roker stage?

653. Which former World Cup winners played in the first World Cup game at Roker Park?

654. Who were the previous World Cup's third-placed team the former winners met in Roker's first match?

655. Roker's second match brought a fixture that would be repeated as a semi-final in the next European Championships in two years' time. Who was it between?

656. The third and final group match at Roker Park was a repeat of a quarter-final from the previous tournament. Who was it between?

657. Roker staged a quarter-final between which two teams?

658. Which other North East ground was used for games in Group Four along with Roker Park?

659. At the 1966 World Cup final, who was the Sunderland chairman who presented the teams to the Queen?

660. In which two tournaments since 1966 has the Stadium of Light been accepted as a host ground, only for England to fail in their bid to stage the tournament?

WORLDWIDE INTERNATIONALS

661. Who was the first Sunderland player to represent an African country?

662. Who was the Honduras international to play for Sunderland?

663. Who was the first Sunderland player to represent the USA?

664. Who was the Sunderland goalkeeper that was a legend in his country of Estonia?

665. Who was the captain of Albania that played for Sunderland?

666. Who was the Sunderland centre-forward that scored for Ghana against England at Wembley?

667. Which goalkeeper won his first 27 caps for Denmark while with Sunderland and went on to win over 100?

668. Who was the first Sunderland player to represent Finland?

669. Who was the striker who scored a dramatic winner against Manchester City and played for South Korea?

670. Which Sweden international broke Charlie Hurley's record as Sunderland's most-capped international?

REPUBLIC OF IRELAND INTERNATIONALS

671. Which player won his 91st cap, but first as a Sunderland player, against Georgia in September 2017?

672. Which player scored against reigning World Champions Germany while on Sunderland's books?

673. Who won all but the first and last of his 40 caps while with Sunderland?

674. Who won 37 of his 110 caps while with Sunderland, including four at the 2002 World Cup?

675. Who won ten caps while with Sunderland, with the next won after his transfer, making him the only player capped while with Hartlepool?

676. Record scorer for his country at the time of his retirement, who scored a third of his 21 international goals while on Sunderland's books?

677. Who scored twice in his two internationals while with Sunderland, both goals coming in a 3-1 win over Turkey in Istanbul in 1991?

678. Which former Manchester City striker won nine caps while with Sunderland, scoring the winner in a 2005 World Cup qualifying game in Cyprus?

679. Which promotion-winning Sunderland captain won seven of his Irish caps while with Sunderland and also signed for his former international manager at the Stadium of Light?

680. When the Republic of Ireland beat the Czech Republic in Dublin in 2002, which other Sunderland player appeared as well as Niall Quinn and Kevin Kilbane?

SCOTLAND INTERNATIONALS

681. Who was the Scots legend who famously taunted World Champions England by doing 'keepy-uppies' as Scotland won at Wembley while he was on Sunderland's books?

682. Of the four Scots in the 1973 FA Cup-winning team, just a single cap was won, by who?

683. Who was the joint top-scorer for Sunderland in 2003-04 (in all competitions), who made his Scotland debut in Busan, South Korea in 2002?

684. The first man to score 100 league goals both sides of the border won just three caps, one while he was with Sunderland. Name him.

685. The first man to be capped by Scotland while with Sunderland is a legendary goalkeeper who is also the only man to be capped while with Arbroath. Who was he?

686. Who scored against England at Hampden a year after captaining Sunderland in their first FA Cup final and to a fifth league title?

687. Who was Sunderland's 1935-36 title winning captain who made his international debut during that season?

688. Which 2000s Sunderland captain played alongside his brother in the first of the five caps he won while with Sunderland?

689. Who is the goalkeeper that is Sunderland's most-capped Scot?

690. Who was the former Aberdeen skipper who played twice for Sunderland in the 2000s and won two caps in that time, the first back at Aberdeen?

JOE BAKER

691   Who did Sunderland sign Baker from in 1969?

692.   How many goals did the former England striker score
       in 24 appearances in the 1969-70 relegation season, none,
       two or four?

693.   Despite hitting ten in 16 games the following season,
       who had been signed to replace Joe as centre-forward?

694.   Which London club did Joe score a hat-trick against
       at Roker Park in 1970?

695.   Which club was Baker with when he won his first five
       England caps?

696.   After 102 goals in 117 league games for his first club which
       Italian team paid £73,000 for him in 1961?

697.   Seven goals in 19 games was good for defensively-minded
       Italy. Which legendary Scotland forward did he play
       alongside in Italy?

698.   What did they call Joe's brother who was a USA international
       and listed Ipswich, Hibs and Man City among his clubs?

699.   In total, Joe played 507 league games in three countries,
       how many league goals did he score, 251, 301 or 351?

700.   Joe's first goal at Roker Park had been for England Under-23s
       against France Under-23s, in which year?

RITCHIE PITT

701. Pitt was the only member of the 1973 FA Cup-winning team to have played at Wembley before the 1973 final. Who had he played for on the first occasion?

702. In the very early stages of the 1973 FA Cup final, who did Ritchie infamously clatter?

703. Which of the clubs beaten on the road to Wembley had Ritchie previously been on loan to?

704. Which national trophy had Pitt won with Sunderland four years before winning the FA Cup?

705. Ritchie made his top-flight debut in a 3-1 defeat at Coventry City in March of which year?

706. Which manager gave Ritchie his debut?

707. How many league games did Ritchie miss in the season before the cup win, none, one or all 42?

708. Who did Bob Stokoe sign to replace him before Ritchie won his place back before the cup was won?

709. Who were Sunderland playing when Pitt suffered a career-ending injury shortly after the cup final?

710. With which fellow injury victim from the same era did Ritchie share a Testimonial against AZ 67?

BOB STOKOE

711. Bob Stokoe became manager of Sunderland in November of which year?

712. His first match was lost to a team managed by the man who would succeed him. Who was that?

713. What change did Stokoe make to the strip in his first match?

714. Which club had he won the FA Cup with as a player?

715. Which club had he been playing for at Roker Park on the day Brian Clough was badly injured?

716. How many of the cup-winning XI did he sign?

717. Which of his cup-winning signings had played for him before?

718. What was he nicknamed at Sunderland?

719. Apart from the FA Cup, which other trophy did Stokoe bring to Roker Park?

720. After resigning in 1976, in which year did he return to Roker as caretaker-manager?

TEAM OF 73

721. In which year did a member of the 1973 FA Cup-winning team first appear in the side?

722. At 20 years and two months, who was the youngest member of the cup final team?

723. How many of the cup-final side went on to win full international honours?

724. In addition to the eleven who played in the final, how many other players appeared during the cup run?

725. How many of the cup-final team scored during the cup-run?

726. Which two players were the leading scorers during the cup-run with four goals each?

727. Who was top scorer in the cup-winning season in all competitions with 19 goals?

728. Who was the caretaker manager who switched Dave Watson from centre-forward to centre-half just before Bob Stokoe took over?

729. Who was the coach of the team who went on to manage Newcastle?

730. Who were the first team the 'Team of 73' met in the 1973-74 European Cup-Winners' Cup?

BILLY HUGHES

731. How many FA Youth Cup finals did Billy play in for Sunderland?

732. Who did he score the winning goal against in the 1973 FA Cup semi-final?

733. Who were Sunderland playing when Billy became the only man to score more than once in a game during the cup run?

734. Which country did he win his solitary international cap against?

735. Which manager described him as the most exciting attacker in Britain after Hughes scored twice against Manchester United at Old Trafford in 1974?

736. That same manager later sold him to Leicester when Billy was leading scorer for which club?

737. Which Californian club did Billy play for in the late seventies?

738. Two years after the cup win, what did Billy do in an FA Cup tie against Chesterfield?

739. Who was his brother that played just once for Sunderland?

740. In which year did Sunderland meet an 'International XI' in a Testimonial for Billy?

DAVE WATSON

741. What was the club record fee Watson was signed for?

742. Who was he signed from?

743. Which position was he signed to play in?

744. What had been his original position at his first club?

745. Who were his first club?

746. Who did he score against during the 1973 FA Cup run?

747. How many England caps did he win as a Sunderland player?

748. When he was sold to Manchester City, which player came to Sunderland in part-exchange?

749. Which German club did he play for?

750. What was the title of the book about Dave, written by his wife?

RICHARD ORD

751. Sunderland won 7-0 on Richard's debut in 1987. Who were they playing?

752. Who did he go on loan to in 1990?

753. Did he play 184, 284 or 384 games for Sunderland?

754. In which season was Richard Player of the Year at Sunderland?

755. What did the club win in the season Richard was Player of the Year?

756. At what level did Richard represent England?

757. He had a testimonial against which former European Cup winners?

758. Which former league club did he manage between 2010 and 2012?

759. Who was he transferred to in 1998?

760. Fill in the missing word.
Who needs _____ when we've got Dickie Ord?

761. Which left-back won the first main Supporters' Association Player of the Year award in 1976-77?

762. Who was the only member of the 1973 FA Cup-winning team to be Player of the Year?

763. Who was Player of the Year in 2016-17 and 2015-16?

764. Who won the award in the year Sunderland reached the 2014 Capital One Cup final?

765. Who won the award in the year Sunderland reached the 1992 FA Cup final?

766. Which forward won the award two years in a row in 1988-89 and 1989-90?

767. Who won in 2002-03 despite not making his debut until January?

768. Which former Oxford midfielder was Player of the Year in the record low points season of 2005-06?

769. Which goalkeeper was Player of the Year in 1984-85 as Sunderland reached the League Cup final, but also went down?

770. Who was Player of the Year in 1986-87 and 1993-94?

QUIZ 78
POP ROBSON

771. What is Pop's real first name?

772. How many spells did he have with Sunderland as a player?

773. In which year did he make his Sunderland debut, 1974, 1979 or 1983?

774. Who did he win the second division title with in 1965?

775. Who did he win the second division title with in 1976?

776. In the season Sunderland won the FA Cup in 1973, Pop was the top-flight's top scorer with which club?

777. How many times was he top scorer in a promotion season for Sunderland?

778. How old was Pop when he became Sunderland's oldest scorer?

779. Was his career total 164, 264 or 364 goals?

780. Why was he called Pop?

GARY ROWELL

781. In which year did Gary score his famous hat-trick away to Newcastle United?

782. Who did he score a top-flight hat-trick against at Roker Park?

783. He is one of how many players to score 100 goals for Sunderland since the Second World War?

784. In the season of his debut, Sunderland won a trophy under which manager?

785. When he was joined in the team by fellow youngsters Shaun Elliott and Kevin Arnott, what were the trio nicknamed?

786. Who was Sunderland's caretaker manager at the time of Gary's hat-trick at St. James' Park?

787. How many times was Gary top, or joint-top scorer in all competitions, five, six or seven?

788. In which year did he score the winning goal as Sunderland won at Liverpool?

789. Of the 22 competitive penalties he took for Sunderland, how many did he score, 20, 21 or 22?

790. At what level was he capped by England?

KEN KNIGHTON

791. When Ken Knighton got the job of Sunderland manager in 1979, which popular long-term manager had fans petitioned to be given the job?

792. What did Knighton achieve in his first season in charge?

793. Which former Newcastle player did Knighton appoint as his assistant manager?

794. Aged only 35 when appointed, Knighton was Sunderland's youngest manager since which Victorian appointment?

795. Which former Sunderland player and future Sunderland manager had he previously been youth team coach for at Sheffield Wednesday?

796. Who did Knighton break Sunderland's transfer record to sign for £300,000 in November 1979?

797. Which Argentinian did he sign for another record fee just a month later?

798. Which former England international right-back was the solitary ever-present in Knighton's promotion-winning side?

799. Which of the following clubs had Knighton NOT played for, Oldham, Preston, Blackburn, Hull, Rotherham or Sheffield Wednesday?

800. Sacked by Sunderland in April 1981, which London club did he become manager of later the same year?

BOLO ZENDEN

801. Which French team did Zenden join Sunderland from?

802. Which club had he started his senior career with in his own country?

803. Which was the first English club he played for?

804. Who had he joined them from?

805. Which North East team did he score the winning goal in a cup final for?

806. Who were the reigning European champions he signed for and played in a Champions League final for?

807. Having joined Sunderland, against which of his former clubs did he lose all of his super-cool image with his attempts to join in an Asamoah Gyan goal celebration?

808. In another failed goal celebration, in which year's World Cup did he fail to complete a somersault after scoring in the third-place match for the Netherlands against Croatia?

809. Against which club did he score one of the best volleys Sunderland have ever scored in a 3-1 win in 2010?

810. Which future Newcastle manager did Zenden serve as assistant manager at Chelsea?

JEFF CLARKE

811. Jeff Clarke arrived at Sunderland in 1975 in part-exchange for which England centre-half?

812. Who was Clarke signed from?

813. In which two years did he win promotion with Sunderland?

814. Against who was he stretchered off shortly before the second of those promotions was sealed?

815. With which England B international did he form a superb central-defensive partnership?

816. Who did Clarke become Player of the Year for after leaving Sunderland on a free transfer?

817. Which foreign country did Jeff go on to play in?

818. Which role did he return to Sunderland in from 1998?

819. Which club did he work for as physio from 2003, remaining in that role as of 2017?

820. Did Jeff play 218, 248 or 288 games for Sunderland?

SHAUN ELLIOTT

821. Which midfield maestro did Shaun debut in the same game as at Wrexham in 1977?

822. Who did Shaun play against for England B at Roker Park?

823. Why did Shaun miss the 1985 League Cup final?

824. Which one of these players made more appearances for Sunderland than Shaun's 358, Michael Gray, Martin Harvey or Len Shackleton?

825. Which manager brought Shaun into the team?

826. Which manager sold him?

827. Which club did he move on to?

828. Which team did he win the Conference with in 1992?

829. Which American team did he go on loan to while he was with Sunderland?

830. He also played in America for a New York based team called Albany Capitals who were managed by which former England and Ipswich striker?

GARY BENNETT

831. Who signed Gary for Sunderland?

832. At which club had the manager who signed him previously, managed Benno?

833. Gary began his career in his home city with which club?

834. Which famous goalkeeper did Gary score against, two minutes into his debut?

835. Against which team did Gary score a dramatic late goal against to take a Play-Off match into extra-time?

836. On the occasion of another of Benno's spectacular late goals, in which year was his late winner against Manchester United that provided Sunderland's first top-flight win in five years?

837. How many times did Gary play at Wembley during the 1990s?

838. What is the name of his brother who won the FA Cup with Coventry in 1987?

839. Gary is one of several players to win the club's official Player of the Year award twice. What sets Benno's pair of wins apart?

840. Which radio commentator did summariser Gary form a long-lasting partnership with on BBC local radio covering Sunderland matches?

1985 LEAGUE CUP

841. Which Sunderland player did the goal deflect in off?

842. Who missed a penalty for Sunderland?

843. Which team were beaten during the cup-run with goals from the player who missed the penalty and the man the goal deflected in off?

844. Which future Sunderland goalkeeper was playing for Norwich in the final?

845. Which future Sunderland manager was playing for Norwich?

846. Rodger Wylde had scored the goals that won Sunderland's first game in the competition. At which club had he previously played for manager Len Ashurst?

847. Who scored the extra-time winner that beat Brian Clough's Nottingham Forest?

848. Who took two penalties in the semi-final, converting one and scoring the other from a rebound?

849. Who had knocked Sunderland out of the League Cup in the two previous seasons?

850. What had been the score when Norwich and Sunderland met at Carrow Road the weekend before the final?

LOAN PLAYERS

851. Who joined Sunderland on loan from Crystal Palace in 2017-18?

852. Which Greek former-Liverpool defender joined on loan from VFL Wolfsburg in 2012?

853. Which Ghana midfielder joined from Internazionale of Milan in 2011?

854. Which Morocco international was signed on loan by Howard Wilkinson from Paris Saint-Germain in 2003?

855. Who was the brother of Simon Grayson's coach Glynn Snodin who joined on loan from Everton in 1994?

856. Who was the Dutch midfielder Alan Durban took on loan from his old club Stoke in 1982?

857. Which goalkeeper came on loan from Notts County when Lawrie McMenemy was manager and returned as goalkeeping coach when Martin O'Neill was in charge?

858. Who came on loan from Fiorentina in 2014, played for Sunderland at Wembley and then won the Premier League with Chelsea in 2017?

859. Who was the Czech Republic defender who joined on loan from Turkish side Trabzonspor in 2013?

860. Which midfielder was on loan from Russian club Rubin Kazan in 2015?

SCANDINAVIANS

861. Who was the Danish forward who debuted as a sub at Chelsea in the first match after promotion in 1999, but never played another League game?

862. Who was the Norway international forward signed for a record fee from Rangers in 2002, who scored against Manchester United on his debut?

863. Prior to the arrival of the Norway forward from Rangers, who was the only other Scandinavian to have cost a record fee, in 1999?

864. Who was the Danish goalkeeper who played just under 200 games between 1998 and 2003?

865. Who was the former Everton and Norway international goalkeeper signed from Turkish club Besiktas in 2002?

866. Which Sweden international scored against England at Euro 92, but was restricted to a single Sunderland game at Aston Villa in 1992?

867. Which Swedish international forward was the son of a former Liverpool defender and made 27 appearances for Sunderland in 2006-07?

868. Which Swedish international forward came on loan from Rennes in 2014-15 to play for one of his former managers Dick Advocaat?

869. Which Sweden international played over 200 games after joining on a free transfer from Birmingham in 2011 and was Player of the Year in 2014-15?

870. Which Swedish player became Sunderland's youngest Premier League player when he played against Middlesbrough in 2016?

THIRD DIVISION

871. When Sunderland were Division Three Champions in 1987-88 who were runners up?

872. Who was top scorer?

873. Which former England striker second top-scored?

874. Which nickname did the front two become known as?

875. Who scored the first and last goal of the season?

876. Who was the first-ever division three fixture against?

877. Which team were beaten away to seal promotion?

878. Who were beaten at Roker on the night the title was secured?

879. Which penalty-taking defender was third top-scorer with 16 goals?

880. Who was the manager who won promotion in his first season?

MARCO GABBIADINI

881. Who was Marco signed from?

882. Which manager signed him?

883. In which English city was he born?

884. What is the name of his brother who once came on as sub for Marco?

885. Which team was he sent-off against moments after scoring a hat-trick?

886. Which team did he score a six-minute hat-trick against a few days before he was sold?

887. Which Newcastle player fouled him when he was brought down for a penalty in the 1990 Play-Offs?

888. Who did he play against for England 'B' at Roker Park?

889. In whose testimonial did he score a hat-trick at the Stadium of Light?

890. In which two successive seasons was he Sunderland's Player of the Year?

1989-90

891. Sunderland played a huge number of competitive games in 1989-90. Were there 57, 58 or 59 games?

892. Who played in all of them?

893. Who missed just one?

894. Which position did Sunderland finish in Division Two?

895. Who were beaten in the Play-Offs?

896. Sunderland lost the Play-Off final only to be promoted when their Wembley conquerors were punished for financial misdemeanours. Which club was that?

897. Apart from the League, Play-Offs, FA Cup and League Cup, which other competition did Sunderland play in?

898. Who was the only man to score in the league and all three cups?

899. Who knocked Sunderland out of the League Cup in a quarter-final replay after Gary Bennett was sent-off in the initial tie for wrestling an opponent into the paddock?

900. Which former England player made his final appearance for Sunderland in the Play-Off final at Wembley?

DENIS SMITH

901. In which year was Denis Smith appointed as Sunderland manager?

902. In which year was he dismissed?

903. Who had he been manager of before taking over at Sunderland?

904. Who was the assistant he brought with him from his previous club?

905. Who was his successor who he brought in as youth coach?

906. How many promotions did Denis win in his first three seasons at Sunderland?

907. Who had he scored for at Sunderland in an FA Cup fifth round replay?

908. Which competition had he won with that club in 1972?

909. Who were his next club after leaving Sunderland?

910. Who was the Arsenal reserve he signed for that club, who went on to play for England and eventually came to Sunderland as a veteran after huge success with Newcastle and Manchester United?

1992 FA CUP

911. The 1992 cup run began with victory over the same club promotion from the third division had been sealed against in 1988. Which club was that?

912. After beating Oxford in the fourth round which London club were faced in the fifth round?

913. Which team were beaten in the quarter-final?

914. Who headed the last-minute goal that won that quarter-final replay?

915. Who were beaten in the semi-final?

916. On which ground was the semi-final played?

917. Who scored in every round leading up to the final?

918. Did it take more, fewer or the same number of games to reach the final than in 1973?

919. Who was caretaker-manager and appointed as permanent boss shortly before the final?

920. Who captained the side, left to join Newcastle and later returned to Sunderland?

1912-13 SEASON

921. This was the greatest season in the history of the club.
Who was the manager?

922. He was from Northern Ireland. How many managers from
that country have won the title since?

923. Sunderland won the title this season, how many league titles
did that mean the club had won?

924. The FA Cup final was reached for the first time.
Who were played in the final?

925. What was the score in the final?

926. The club's all-time leading league goal-scorer top-scored
that season. Who was he?

927. In February of that year, Sunderland won at Middlesbrough,
although they were without their England internationals
who were playing Northern Ireland. Never has an England
team contained as many Sunderland players. How many
were there in the England side?

928. Who was the team's captain, capped by Scotland
that season?

929. How many times did Sunderland lose to Newcastle
in the five meetings they had with them in 1912-13?

930. Sunderland won the league despite a bad start. How many
points were taken from the first seven games, two, three or four?

SOUTH AMERICANS

931. Which Argentinian became Sunderland's first South American player when signed for a record fee in 1979?

932. Who was the Argentinian who scored on his debut against West Ham in 2000?

933. Which Argentinian defender was signed by Steve Bruce, made his debut against Manchester United on Boxing Day 2010, but hardly played?

934. Who was the player from Paraguay who debuted on the night Andy Reid scored twice in a 4-1 League Cup win at Norwich?

935. Which Paraguay midfielder scored at the 2010 World Cup after signing for Sunderland, but before his debut?

936. Nicknamed 'Bica', who was the Brazilian forward who played once for Sunderland in 1999 after signing from a club in Peru?

937. Nicknamed 'The Wall' who was the Brazilian defender signed for a record fee in 2000?

938. Which Argentinian forward scored five goals for River Plate in the semi-final of the Copa Libertadores in September 2017?

939. Who was the Argentinian international whose spectacular own-goal set Sunderland en-route to a record-equalling 8-0 defeat at Southampton in 2014?

940. Which Head Coach led Sunderland to Wembley in 2014?

QUIZ 95

CARIBBEAN & CENTRAL AMERICAN PLAYERS

941. Which two-time Player of the Year has a Foundation in his family's home of St. Lucia?

942. Which Guadaloupe-born defender was signed from and sold to Tottenham Hotspur?

943. Which Honduras international became the first man from his country to play in the Premiership when he debuted for Sunderland in 2000?

944. Of the four players from Trinidad and Tobago to play for the club, who was the first?

945. Which player from Trinidad and Tobago was Player of the Year in 2008?

946. Which Trinidad and Tobago player was signed from Coventry and sold to Southampton?

947. Who was the first man from Costa Rica to play for Sunderland?

948. Which Caribbean-born player scored a stunning goal against Burnley in 2007 that all but sealed Sunderland's promotion?

949. Have players won more caps for Paraguay or Trinidad and Tobago while on Sunderland's books?

950. Which Caribbean country did London-born Nyron Nosworthy represent?

ROKER PARK

951. In which year did Roker Park open?

952. In which year did it close?

953. Which team did Sunderland play in the first and final matches at the ground?

954. Which team did Sunderland play in the last league game at the ground?

955. How many times did England play a full international at the ground?

956. How many times did the USSR play a full international at the ground?

957. Who did Sunderland play at Roker Park in the club's Centenary match in 1979?

958. In the 1972-73 season, which FA Cup tie went to extra-time at Roker Park?

959. On the night of the final match at Roker Park, which legendary player dug up the centre-spot to transfer it to the Stadium of Light?

960. Was the record attendance, 6,000, 16,000 or 26,000 more than the Stadium of Light's capacity following its North Stand extension?

961. Who did Sunderland play in the first match at the Stadium of Light?

962. Who were the first league visitors?

963. Who was the first opponent to score at the stadium?

964. Who were the first visiting team to win at the stadium?

965. Who did Sunderland play in the stadium's first cup-tie?

966. Who was the first Sunderland player sent-off at the Stadium of Light, against Chelsea in October 2000?

967. In 2001, the Stadium of Light staged the European Championships Under-16 final between which countries?

968. In the first two decades of the Stadium of Light, who did England play in the only Under-21 international played at the ground?

969. What connects Kevin Keegan, Sven-Goran Eriksson and Roy Hodgson at the Stadium of Light?

970. In which year did the North Stand extension open?

PETER REID

971. In which year did Peter Reid become Sunderland manager?

972. In which year did he play for Bolton Wanderers at Roker Park on a day when Sunderland won promotion?

973. In which year did he manage Manchester City against Sunderland on a day they were relegated?

974. How many times did Peter Reid win a trophy with Sunderland?

975. As a player, how many England caps did he win, 13, 23 or 33?

976. Reid was the Players' Player of the Year in a season his club, Everton won the League and a European trophy. Which year was that?

977. What did Michel Platini, Preban Elkjaer and Diego Maradona beat Reid to in 1985?

978. Which other team did Peter manage for part of his time as Sunderland manager?

979. Which international team did he go on to manage?

980. How many times did he smash the Sunderland transfer record?

105 POINT SEASON

981. In which season did Sunderland achieve this record?

982. Kevin Phillips, Niall Quinn and who else got into double figures in league goals?

983. How many players appeared in every league game?

984. Thomas Sorensen and which other player debuted in the opening game of the season?

985. Who were the only team to beat Sunderland at the Stadium of Light in the league?

986. Which team were beaten 7-0?

987. In which competition did Sunderland reach the semi-final?

988. How many games were still to be played when promotion was mathematically confirmed?

989. Which club finished as runners-up?

990. In all competitions, did Sunderland score more or fewer goals than the number of points achieved?

SUPERKEV

991. Which club released Kevin Phillips as a young player?

992. Which club did Sunderland sign him from?

993. How many goals did he score for the club, 110, 120 or 130?

994. How many times did he score four goals in a game for Sunderland?

995. How many other hat-tricks did he score?

996. When he made his England debut which Sunderland teammate debuted in the same game?

997. Whose post-war seasonal goal-scoring record did he break at Sunderland?

998. Whose post-war overall goal-scoring record did he break?

999. In which season did he win the European Golden Shoe as the continent's top scorer?

1000. Against which club did SuperKev score his 100th Sunderland goal against?

ANSWERS

QUIZ 1 · GOALKEEPERS

1. Jim Montgomery
2. Johnny Mapson
3. Albert McInroy
4. Simon Mignolet
5. Tony Norman
6. Joe Butler
7. Tony Coton
8. Lionel Perez
9. Ben Alnwick
10. Craig Gordon

QUIZ 2 · ENGLAND AT THE SOL

11. Belgium
12. 1999
13. Michael Gray
14. Under-16
15. 2003
16. Darius Vassell
17. Slovakia
18. Australia
19. Marcus Rashford
20. Eric Dier

QUIZ 3 · JOE BOLTON

21. Left-back
22. 1972

23. Yes
24. Charlton
25. Four
26. The Division Two title
27. 1976
28. Alan Durban
29. Sheffield United
30. Matlock Town

QUIZ 4 · STAN ANDERSON

31. Three
32. 1952
33. Arsenal
34. Bulgaria
35. Two
36. Two
37. Newcastle United
38. Newcastle United
39. AEK Athens
40. Peter Reid and Sam Allardyce

QUIZ 5 · CHARLIE HURLEY

41. Alan Brown
42. Alan Brown
43. Three
44. 1964-65

45. Reading
46. Bobby Moore
47. 1963-64
48. The Charlie Hurley gates
49. Seb Larsson
50. Player of the Century

QUIZ 6 · LEE CATTERMOLE

51. Middlesbrough
52. Seville
53. Wigan Athletic
54. Steve Bruce
55. 2009
56. Bolton
57. Lorik Cana
58. Tottenham Hotspur
59. 2009
60. 2014

QUIZ 7 · BOBBY KERR

61. The Little General
62. 1966
63. Manchester City
64. Seven
65. Reading
66. The only two men to lift the FA Cup as Sunderland captain
67. George Kerr
68. Blackpool
69. Hartlepool
70. Birmingham City

QUIZ 8 · COLIN SUGGETT

71. 1967
72. The FA Youth Cup in 1967
73. 90
74. 25
75. WBA
76. Norwich City
77. Newcastle United
78. The League Cup
79. The League Cup again
80. Southampton

QUIZ 9 · BOBBY GURNEY

81. 228
82. 390
83. Silksworth
84. Seven
85. 31
86. Preston North End
87. One
88. Peterborough United
89. Liverpool
90. Four

QUIZ 10 · IAN PORTERFIELD

91. Raith Rovers
92. 1967-68
93. Right
94. The Impossible Dream
95. Reading
96. Sheffield Wednesday

97. Alex Ferguson
98. Chelsea
99. Zambia
100. Armenia

QUIZ 11 · DENNIS TUEART

101. Three
102. Swindon Town
103. 1968
104. Manchester City
105. 1971-72
106. Vasas Budapest
107. Tony Towers
108. Newcastle United
109. Finland
110. Pele

QUIZ 12 · SUBS

111. David Young
112. Mike Hellawell
113. 1965
114. Alan Gauden
115. Mike Hellawell
116. Ian McColl
117. George Herd
118. Malcolm Moore
119. Jimmy Hamilton
120. Ji

QUIZ 13 · AIDEN McGEADY

121. Derby County

122. Norwich City
123. Preston North End
124. 2004
125. Martin O'Neill
126. 2007-08
127. Republic of Ireland
128. Spartak Moscow
129. Everton
130. Sheffield United

QUIZ 14 · 2014 CAPITAL ONE CUP

131. Manchester City
132. Vito Mannone
133. Fabio Borini
134. Ten minutes
135. Yaya Toure
136. Jesus Navas
137. Ki Sung Yueng
138. David Moyes
139. Southampton
140. MK Dons

QUIZ 15 · BRENDAN GALLOWAY

141. Everton
142. MK Dons
143. 2015
144. Everton 6-2 Sunderland
145. West Brom
146. Kenny Swain
147. Derby County

148. 15

149. 2015

150. One of his middle names is Zibusiso and he was born in Zimbabwe

QUIZ 16 · JOHN O'SHEA

151. Steve Bruce

152. Tottenham Hotspur

153. Two

154. Five

155. He scored a last minute equaliser

156. Five

157. Bournemouth

158. Royal Antwerp

159. 2011

160. Anton Ferdinand

QUIZ 17 · NIALL QUINN

161. 1991

162. Leicester City

163. Nottingham Forest

164. Manchester City

165. Stockport County

166. Bradford City

167. Derby County

168. Holland

169. West Bromwich Albion

170. One (SuperKev)

QUIZ 18 · SIMON GRAYSON

171. He played against Sunderland for Leicester City at Roker Park

172. None

173. Jackie Ashurst

174. Middlesbrough

175. Blackpool

176. Blackpool

177. Four

178. Six

179. Lee Clark

180. George Honeyman

QUIZ 19 · DERBY GAMES

181. Six

182. Nine

183. Gary Rowell

184. Wayne Entwistle

185. Eric Gates and Marco Gabbiadini

186. Thomas Sorensen

187. 10%

188. Jermain Defoe

189. 2008

190. Newcastle United 1 Sunderland 9

QUIZ 20 · DEBUTS

191. Dominic Matteo

192. John Hughes

193. Ronnie Turnbull
194. Seven
195. Alan Spence
196. Darren Bent
197. Djibril Cisse
198. Craig Gordon
199. Martyn Waghorn
200. Derek Forster

QUIZ 21 · NICK SUMMERBEE

201. 100
202. Craig Russell
203. Mike
204. His Grandad, George. (Nick's Great Uncle Gordon had also played in the league)
205. Portsmouth
206. Charlton Athletic
207. Swindon Town
208. Bolton Wanderers
209. Bradford City
210. Both

QUIZ 22 · JOHNNY CROSSAN

211. 22
212. None
213. Standard Liege
214. Under (99)
215. Manchester United
216. Manchester City
217. Middlesbrough

218. 11
219. Uruguay
220. 30

QUIZ 23 · WILLIE WATSON

221. Cricket
222. 12
223. None
224. Wales
225. Huddersfield Town
226. Huddersfield Town
227. Halifax Town (Then a league club)
228. Bradford City
229. South Africa
230. 1950

QUIZ 24 · STAN CUMMINS

231. West Ham
232. Liverpool
233. Burnley
234. 1979-80
235. Ken Knighton
236. Claudio Marangoni
237. Jackie Charlton
238. Crystal Palace
239. Seattle Sounders
240. Brian Clough

QUIZ 25 · DICKIE DAVIS

241. 25
242. 1949-50

243. He had signed just before the start of the Second World War

244. Trevor Ford

245. 80

246. Darlington

247. Aston Villa

248. Two

249. Derby County 6 Sunderland 5

250. Kevin Phillips

QUIZ 26 · KEVIN BALL

251. Denis Smith

252. Portsmouth

253. Gary Lineker and Paul Gascoigne

254. Twice

255. 1996-97

256. Sheffield United - and also a converted penalty in the shoot-out with Charlton

257. Coventry City

258. Fulham and Burnley

259. Jordan Henderson

260. Peterborough United

QUIZ 27 · COLIN TODD

261. Everton's Goodison Park

262. 1966

263. Stamford Bridge against Chelsea

264. Sunderland's record defeat of 8-0 was equalled at West Ham

265. £170,000

266. Brian Clough

267. Two

268. PFA Player of the Year

269. More

270. 27

QUIZ 28 · JOHNNY COCHRANE

271. He is the only man to win the League title, FA Cup and Charity Shield

272. The FA Cup semi-final

273. 1934-35

274. 1935-36

275. 1936-37

276. Arsenal

277. St. Johnstone

278. Reading

279. St. Mirren

280. 1928

QUIZ 29 · THOMAS SORENSEN

281. 29

282. Andy Marriott

283. Lionel Perez

284. Tony Coton

285. Everton

286. Leicester City

287. Niall Quinn

288. 2001

289. Defending World
     Champions France

290. Jim McNab

QUIZ 30 · JORDAN PICKFORD

291. Eight

292. Bradford City

293. Six

294. Simon Grayson at Preston

295. Preston

296. Jim Montgomery

297. Albert McInroy

298. Joel Campbell

299. Five

300. The Europa League

QUIZ 31 · TONY TOWERS

301. Manchester City

302. Scored and been sent-off

303. 1970

304. Wolves

305. Dennis Tueart
     and Mick Horswill

306. Ten

307. Lord Westwood

308. Three

309. Jimmy Adamson

310. Vic Halom

QUIZ 32 · FASTEST TO 50 GOALS

311. Johnny Campbell

312. David Halliday

313. Brian Clough

314. Jamie Millar

315. Kevin Phillips

316. Charlie Fleming

317. James Hannah

318. Trevor Ford

319. Nick Sharkey

320. Marco Gabbiadini

QUIZ 33 · JULIO ARCA

321. Argentina

322. Middlesbrough

323. South Shields

324. West Ham

325. Emerson Thome

326. 2006

327. Ghana

328. Argentinos Juniors

329. Craven Cottage, where
     Arca played an Under-21
     international against
     England.

330. Mark Paston

QUIZ 34 · RECORD SIGNINGS

331. Ally McCoist

332. Niall Quinn

333. Lee Clark

334. Craig Gordon

335. Darren Bent

336. Dave Watson

337. Bob Lee

338. Len Shackleton

339. Alf Common

340. Stefan Schwarz

QUIZ 35 · ENGLAND INTERNATIONALS

341. Jermain Defoe

342. Nick Pickering

343. Stan Anderson

344. Fraizer Campbell

345. Jordan Henderson

346. Gavin McCann

347. George Holley

348. Dave Watson

349. Tom Porteous

350. Willie Watson

QUIZ 36 · 1936 CHAMPIONS

351. Six

352. None

353. It left Sunderland as the only club to have only ever played at the top level

354. Johnny Cochrane

355. Bobby Gurney and Raich Carter

356. None

357. Over (109)

358. Arsenal

359. Derby County

360. Jimmy Thorpe

QUIZ 37 · 1937 FA CUP WINNERS

361. Preston North End

362. 3-1

363. Bill Shankly

364. Raich Carter

365. Bobby Gurney

366. Eddie Burbanks

367. Millwall

368. Patsy Gallacher

369. Wolves

370. Manchester City

QUIZ 38 · THE 2017-18 SEASON

371. Simon Grayson

372. Derby County

373. Lewis Grabban

374. Bury

375. George Honeyman

376. Lynden Gooch

377. Paul Heckingbottom

378. Daryl Murphy

379. The Bradley Lowery Foundation

380. Martyn Waghorn

QUIZ 39 · JONNY WILLIAMS

381. Crystal Palace
382. Wales
383. He was Palace's Young Player of the Year
384. Ipswich Town
385. Mick McCarthy
386. Nottingham Forest
387. MK Dons
388. Seven
389. Sheffield United
390. Euro 2016

QUIZ 40 · LEWIS GRABBAN

391. Crystal Palace
392. Millwall
393. Andy Scott
394. Bournemouth
395. Norwich City
396. Bournemouth
397. Reading
398. Norwich City
399. Motherwell
400. 11

QUIZ 41 · JAMES VAUGHAN

401. Hull City
402. David Moyes
403. James Milner
404. Wayne Rooney
405. Joe Royle

406. Under-21
407. Jamaica
408. Derby County
409. Huddersfield Town
410. 24

QUIZ 42 · VIC HALOM

411. Nine
412. Manchester City
413. Arsenal
414. Derby County
415. Hungary
416. Division two title in 1976
417. Rotherham United
418. Luton Town
419. Eric Morecambe
420. The Liberal Democrats

QUIZ 43 · DAVID HALLIDAY

421. 43
422. 1928-29
423. Four
424. None
425. None
426. Four
427. St. Mirren
428. Arsenal
429. Manchester City
430. Halliday was manager of Leicester whose final day win at Birmingham condemned Sunderland to relegation

QUIZ 44 · NORTHERN IRELAND INTERNATIONALS

431. Paddy McNair
432. Jonny Evans
433. McConnell
434. Billy Bingham
435. Ian Lawther
436. Martin Harvey
437. Martin Harvey, Johnny Crossan and John Parke
438. John Parke
439. Phil Gray
440. George McCartney

QUIZ 45 · WALES INTERNATIONALS

441. Adam Matthews and Jonny Williams
442. David Vaughan
443. Carl Robinson
444. John Oster
445. Andy Melville
446. Colin Pascoe
447. Leighton James
448. Ray Daniel
449. Trevor Ford
450. L.R. Roose

QUIZ 46 · LEN ASHURST

451. The highest number of appearances by an outfield player

452. Left-back
453. Left Back In Time
454. 1984-85
455. Four
456. The Lion
457. Cec Irwin and Jimmy McNab
458. 458
459. England Youths
460. Newport County

QUIZ 47 · GEORGE HERD

461. Scotland
462. 15
463. He never played for Sunderland again
464. The Scottish Cup
465. Hartlepool
466. Jim Montgomery
467. 318
468. 1969
469. Kuwait
470. Sunderland RCA

QUIZ 48 · JORDAN HENDERSON

471. Chelsea's Stamford Bridge
472. Falkirk
473. Manchester City
474. Steve Bruce
475. Manchester City 4 Sunderland 3

476. Wigan Athletic
477. 2011
478. Coventry City
479. Four
480. Australia

QUIZ 49 · STEPHANE SESSEGNON

481. Paris Saint-Germain
482. Sunderland
483. Paolo Di Canio
484. West Brom
485. Sunderland
486. 2011-12
487. Three
488. Lionel Messi and Pele
489. Montpellier
490. Benin

QUIZ 50 · THE 1949-50 SEASON

491. One
492. Third
493. Portsmouth
494. Once
495. Manchester City
496. Dickie Davis
497. Bill Murray
498. 68,004 (The record FA Cup attendance is 75,118)
499. Jack Stelling
500. Tommy Wright and Tommy Reynolds

QUIZ 51 · THE BANK OF ENGLAND TEAM

501. The 1950s
502. 1949-50
503. Trevor Ford
504. Billy Bingham
505. Manchester City
506. Birmingham City
507. Bill Murray
508. Being found guilty of illegal payments in the days of the maximum wage
509. Nothing
510. Relegation in 1958 was the first in the club's history

QUIZ 52 · TREVOR FORD

511. 70
512. Aston Villa
513. Sheffield Wednesday
514. 23
515. PSV Eindhoven
516. Because he was banned by the FA having been involved in the illegal payments scandal that rocked, 'The Bank of England Club'
517. George Hardwick
518. He scored the winner
519. Ivor Allchurch

520.   Gary Sobers

QUIZ 53 · LEN SHACKLETON

521.   'The Average Director's Knowledge of Football'

522.   Forever. He was never picked again

523.   Arsenal

524.   Bradford Park Avenue

525.   Six

526.   Because a Sunderland director had been tipped off by a Newcastle director that the top bid was £20,000

527.   £13,000, 0.3d - that is £13,000 and three old pence

528.   101

529.   The Clown Prince of Soccer

530.   Alan Brown

QUIZ 54 · YOUNGEST PLAYERS

531.   Derek Forster

532.   15

533.   Jimmy Hamilton

534.   16

535.   Cec Irwin

536.   Rob Hindmarch

537.   Nick Sharkey

538.   Jimmy Thorpe

539.   Martyn Waghorn

540.   Joel Asoro

QUIZ 55 · OLDEST PLAYERS

541.   Thomas Urwin

542.   Bryan 'Pop' Robson

543.   Brian Deane

544.   Colin Cooper

545.   Chris Waddle

546.   Wimbledon

547.   Steve Bould

548.   Dwight Yorke

549.   Andy Cole

550.   Tony Coton

QUIZ 56 · CHARLIE BUCHAN

551.   209

552.   222

553.   Four

554.   Liverpool

555.   1927

556.   1912-13

557.   1912-13

558.   He was the country's leading scorer

559.   Arsenal

560.   Charles Buchan's Football Monthly

QUIZ 57 · RAICH CARTER

561.   Horatio Stratton Carter

562.   Leicester City

563.   Four

564.   1932-33

565. Bobby Gurney

566. 31

567. Three

568. Second

569. Derby County

570. Win the FA Cup

QUIZ 58 · MICHAEL GRAY

571. Just one,
Gordon Armstrong

572. Barnsley

573. 1992-93

574. Martin and Phil

575. Dariusz Kubicki

576. 1996-97

577. Liverpool

578. Three

579. Allan Johnston

580. Celtic

QUIZ 59 · GORDON ARMSTRONG

581. 59

582. 1989-90

583. Six

584. Debut

585. 1992-93

586. Peter Davenport

587. Division Three
Championship 1987-88

588. Bristol City

589. Bury

590. Chris

QUIZ 60 · PLAYED ONCE

591. Peter Barnes

592. John Hughes

593. Alan Hay

594. Nicholas Medina

595. Jan Eriksson

596. Ricardo Gabbiadini

597. Dick Huntley

598. Marcos Di Guiseppe (Bica)

599. Jonjo Dickman

600. Dominic Matteo

QUIZ 61 · JIM MONTGOMERY

601. None

602. 1961

603. Derby County

604. None

605. Sandy McLaughlan

606. Four

607. There hadn't been one. It
was Jim's first FA Cup clean
sheet away from Roker

608. Brian Clough

609. Nottingham Forest

610. 33

QUIZ 62 · 2006-07 PROMOTION

611. Niall Quinn

612. Roy Keane

613. David Connolly
614. Nyron Nosworthy
615. None
616. March
617. Burnley
618. Crystal Palace
619. Luton Town
620. Preston North End

QUIZ 63 · BRIAN CLOUGH

621. 63
622. Bury
623. Bob Stokoe
624. 28
625. Middlesbrough
626. Leeds United
627. Hartlepool United
628. Derby County
629. Nottingham Forest
630. Malcolm Bramley

QUIZ 64 · THE FIRST PROMOTION SEASON

631. Charlton Athletic
632. Grimsby Town
633. Leeds United
634. Four
635. Charlie Hurley
636. Johnny Crossan
637. Everton

638. Manchester United
639. Alan Brown
640. 1963-64

QUIZ 65 · THE SECOND PROMOTION SEASON

641. 1975-76
642. Bob Stokoe
643. Six
644. 6th round, or quarter-final
The same stage reached
by the 1964 team
645. Bristol City
646. Pop Robson
647. Gary Rowell
648. Anglo-Scottish Cup
649. Jeff Clarke
650. Sam Allardyce

QUIZ 66 · THE WORLD CUP

651. July
652. Four
653. Italy
654. Chile
655. Italy and the USSR
656. Chile and the USSR
657. Hungary and the USSR
658. Middlesbrough FC's
Ayresome Park
659. Syd Collings
660. 2006 and 2018

QUIZ 67 · WORLDWIDE INTERNATIONALS

661. Reuben Agboola for Nigeria
662. Milton Nunez
663. Claudio Reyna
664. Mart Poom
665. Lorik Cana
666. Asamoah Gyan
667. Thomas Sorensen
668. Teemu Tainio
669. Ji Dong-won
670. Seb Larsson

QUIZ 68 · REPUBLIC OF IRELAND INTERNATIONALS

671. Aiden McGeady
672. John O'Shea
673. Charlie Hurley
674. Kevin Kilbane
675. Ambrose Fogarty
676. Niall Quinn
677. John Byrne
678. Stephen Elliott
679. Gary Breen
680. Paul Butler

QUIZ 69 · SCOTLAND INTERNATIONALS

681. Jim Baxter
682. Billy Hughes
683. Kevin Kyle
684. Neil Martin
685. Ted Doig
686. Charlie Thomson
687. Alex Hastings
688. Steve Caldwell
689. Craig Gordon
690. Russell Anderson

QUIZ 70 · JOE BAKER

691. Nottingham Forest
692. Two
693. Dave Watson
694. Charlton Athletic
695. Hibernians
696. Torino
697. Denis Law
698. Gerry
699. 301
700. 1959

QUIZ 71 · RITCHIE PITT

701. England schoolboys
702. Allan Clarke
703. Arsenal
704. The FA Youth Cup
705. 1969
706. Alan Brown
707. One
708. David Young

709. Luton Town

710. Bobby Park

QUIZ 72 · BOB STOKOE

711. 1972

712. Jimmy Adamson of Burnley

713. He reinstated black shorts instead of white ones.

714. Newcastle United

715. Bury

716. Two

717. Vic Halom

718. The Messiah

719. The Second Division title in 1976

720. 1987

QUIZ 73 · TEAM OF 73

721. 1961, Jim Montgomery

722. Mick Horswill

723. Three: Watson, Hughes and Tueart

724. Six: Young, Tones, Lathan, McGiven, Bolton and J. Ashurst. (Chambers and Coleman had been unused subs)

725. Eight

726. Dave Watson and Billy Hughes

727. Billy Hughes

728. Billy Elliott

729. Arthur Cox

730. Vasas Budapest

QUIZ 74 · BILLY HUGHES

731. Two

732. Arsenal

733. Manchester City

734. Sweden

735. Tommy Docherty

736. Derby County

737. San Jose Earthquakes

738. He went in goal when Jim Montgomery was injured

739. John Hughes

740. 1977

QUIZ 75 · DAVE WATSON

741. £100,000

742. Rotherham United

743. Centre-forward

744. Centre-half

745. Notts County

746. Luton Town

747. 14

748. Jeff Clarke

749. Werder Bremen

750. My Dear Watson

QUIZ 76 · RICHARD ORD

751. Southend United

752. York City

753. 284
754. 1995-96
755. The Division One title
756. Under-21
757. Steaua Bucharest
758. Durham City
759. QPR
760. Cantona

QUIZ 77 · PLAYER OF THE YEAR

761. Joe Bolton
762. Bobby Kerr
763. Jermain Defoe
764. Vito Mannone
765. John Byrne
766. Marco Gabbiadini
767. Sean Thornton
768. Dean Whitehead
769. Chris Turner
770. Gary Bennett

QUIZ 78 · POP ROBSON

771. Bryan
772. Three
773. 1974
774. Newcastle United
775. Sunderland
776. West Ham United
777. Twice
778. 38 (and 182 days)
779. 264

780. As a child he was one of three friends nick-named Snap, Crackle and Pop after a Rice Krispies breakfast cereal slogan

QUIZ 79 · GARY ROWELL

781. 1979
782. Arsenal
783. Three
784. Bob Stokoe (1976 Div Two title)
785. Charlie's Angels (after the Sunderland scout Charlie Ferguson and the Charlie's Angels TV series)
786. Billy Elliott
787. Six
788. 1983
789. 21
790. England Under-21

QUIZ 80 · KEN KNIGHTON

791. Billy Elliott
792. Promotion
793. Frank Clark
794. Robert Campbell
795. Len Ashurst
796. Stan Cummins
797. Claudio Marangoni
798. Steve Whitworth
799. Rotherham

800. Orient

QUIZ 81 · BOLO ZENDEN

801. Marseille

802. PSV Eindhoven

803. Chelsea

804. Barcelona

805. Middlesbrough

806. Liverpool

807. Chelsea

808. 1998

809. Spurs

810. Rafa Benitez

QUIZ 82 · JEFF CLARKE

811. Dave Watson

812. Manchester City

813. 1976 and 1980

814. Cardiff

815. Shaun Elliott

816. Newcastle United

817. Turkey

818. Academy physio

819. Dundee United

820. 218

QUIZ 83 · SHAUN ELLIOTT

821. Kevin Arnott

822. Spain

823. He was suspended

824. Michael Gray

825. Jimmy Adamson

826. Lawrie McMenemy

827. Norwich City

828. Colchester United

829. Seattle Sounders

830. Paul Mariner

QUIZ 84 · GARY BENNETT

831. Len Ashurst

832. Cardiff City

833. Manchester City

834. Peter Shilton

835. Gillingham

836. 1990

837. Three

838. Dave

839. His awards in 1987 and 1994 were the furthest apart

840. Nick Barnes

QUIZ 85 · 1985 LEAGUE CUP

841. Gordon Chisholm

842. Clive Walker

843. Tottenham Hotspur

844. Chris Woods

845. Steve Bruce

846. Sheffield Wednesday

847. Howard Gayle

848. Colin West

849. Norwich City

850. Norwich 1-3 Sunderland

QUIZ 86 · LOAN PLAYERS

851. Jonny Williams
852. Sotirios Kyrgiakos
853. Sulley Muntari
854. Talal El Karkouri
855. Ian Snodin
856. Loek Ursem
857. Seamus (Jim) McDonagh
858. Marcos Alonso
859. Ondrej Celustka
860. Yann M'Vila

QUIZ 87 · SCANDINAVIANS

861. Carsten Fredgaard
862. Tore Andre Flo
863. Stefan Schwarz
864. Thomas Sorensen
865. Thomas Myhre
866. Jan Eriksson
867. Toby Hysen
868. Ola Toivonen
869. Seb Larsson
870. Joel Asoro

QUIZ 88 · THIRD DIVISION

871. Brighton and Hove Albion
872. Marco Gabbiadini
873. Eric Gates
874. The G-Force
875. Keith Bertschin
876. Brentford

877. Port Vale
878. Northampton Town
879. John MacPhail
880. Denis Smith

QUIZ 89 · MARCO GABBIADINI

881. York City
882. Denis Smith
883. Nottingham
884. Ricardo
885. Ipswich Town
886. Charlton Athletic
887. Mark Stimson
888. Czechoslovakia B
889. Jim McNab
890. 1988-89 and 1989-90

QUIZ 90 · 1989-90

891. 59
892. Gordon Armstrong
893. Marco Gabbiadini
894. Sixth
895. Newcastle United
896. Swindon Town
897. The Zenith Data Systems Cup
898. Gordon Armstrong
899. Coventry City
900. Eric Gates

QUIZ 91 · DENIS SMITH

901. 1987

902. 1991

903. York City

904. Viv Busby

905. Malcolm Crosby

906. Two

907. Stoke City

908. The League Cup

909. Bristol City

910. Andy Cole

QUIZ 92 · 1992 FA CUP

911. Port Vale

912. West Ham United

913. Chelsea

914. Gordon Armstrong

915. Norwich City

916. Hillsborough

917. John Byrne

918. Fewer

919. Malcolm Crosby

920. Paul Bracewell

QUIZ 93 · 1912-13 SEASON

921. Bob Kyle

922. None

923. Five

924. Aston Villa

925. Aston Villa 1-0 Sunderland

926. Charlie Buchan

927. Three: Buchan, Jackie Mordue and Francis Cuggy

928. Charlie Thomson

929. None

930. Two

QUIZ 94 · SOUTH AMERICANS

931. Claudio Marangoni

932. Julio Arca

933. Marcos Angeleri

934. Paolo Da Silva

935. Cristian Riveros

936. Marcos Di Guiseppe

937. Emerson Thome

938. Ignacio Scocco

939. Santiago Vergini

940. Gus Poyet

QUIZ 95 · CARIBBEAN AND CENTRAL AMERICAN PLAYERS

941. Jermain Defoe

942. Pascal Chimbonda

943. Milton Nunez

944. Dwight Yorke

945. Kenwyne Jones

946. Stern John

947. Bryan Oviedo

948. Carlos Edwards

949. Paraguay

950. Jamaica

QUIZ 96 · ROKER PARK

951. 1898

952. 1997

953. Liverpool
954. Everton
955. Three
956. Three
957. An England XI
958. A first round, second replay between Hartlepool United and Scunthorpe
959. Charlie Hurley
960. 26,000

QUIZ 97 · STADIUM OF LIGHT

961. Ajax
962. Manchester City
963. Giorgio Kinkladze
964. Norwich City
965. Bury
966. Kevin Kilbane
967. Spain and Italy
968. Slovakia
969. They have all managed England at the stadium
970. 2000

QUIZ 98 · PETER REID

971. 1995
972. 1976
973. 1991
974. Two
975. 13
976. 1985
977. They were the top three in the World Player of the Year award in which Reid was fourth
978. He was manager of England Under-21s
979. Thailand
980. Six (Quinn, Clark, Schwarz, Thome, Reyna and Flo)

QUIZ 99 · 105 POINT SEASON

981. 1998-99
982. Danny Dichio
983. None
984. Paul Butler
985. Barnsley
986. Oxford United
987. The League Cup
988. Four
989. Bradford City
990. More (108 to 105)

QUIZ 100 · SUPERKEV

991. Southampton
992. Watford
993. 130
994. Twice
995. Two
996. Michael Gray
997. Brian Clough
998. Gary Rowell
999. 1999-2000
1000. Bolton Wanderers